BE FABULOUS AT ANY AGE

CREATING AGELESS SKIN THROUGH SEASONAL LIVING

Be Fabulous At Any Age:

Creating Ageless Skin Through Seasonal Living   Second Edition

Copyright © 2011 and 2014 Elisabeth L. Thieriot.

All rights reserved.

Published by Lions Gate Corporation

San Francisco, California, USA

First Printing September 2011

Second Edition Printing January 2014

ISBN 978-0-9839408-2-1

Library of Congress Cataloging-in-Publication Data:

Thieriot, Elisabeth.

Be Fabulous at Any Age: Creating Ageless Skin Through Seasonal Living / Elisabeth Thieriot

Includes bibliographical references and index.

ISBN-13: 978-0-9839408-2-1

2011916657

10 9 8 7 6 5 4 3 2 1

BE FABULOUS AT ANY AGE

CREATING AGELESS SKIN THROUGH SEASONAL

LIVING

ELISABETH L. THIERIOT

Lions Gate Corporation

One Sansome Street, Suite 3500, San Francisco, CA 94104

The author of this book is not providing medical advice or prescribing the use of any technique as a form of treatment for physical, emotional, or medical problems. The intent of this author is only to offer information of a general nature to help you understand the importance of living a life according to the seasons. In the event you use any of the information in this book for yourself, the author and publisher assume no responsibility for your actions. The publisher and author are not liable for any damages or negative consequences from any action, application, or preparations to any person reading or following the information in this book. References are provided for informational purposes only and do not constitute endorsement of any websites or other sources. Readers should be aware that the websites listed in this book might change.

Additional copies of this publication may be obtained by visiting

www.befabulousatanyage.com.

Visit **www.elisabeththieriot.com** for seasonal

living information. For seasonal skin care products,

please visit **www.repleteskincare.com.**

ENDORSEMENTS

"Elisabeth Thieriot, always a vision of style, has become a voice of reason and inspiration in her philosophy for creating ageless skin and glamour through seasonal living." — Tatiana Sorokko, Model and Author

"This book is a fantastic idea, full of truth and common sense; in other words, wisdom! I hope everybody reads it. I really believe in all this and always have." — Prince Dimitri of Yugoslavia

"Growing up in Europe with real seasons, this book reminded me of all the things my mother told me about a healthy lifestyle. Elisabeth's book will occupy a primary spot in my library for sure." — Hans H. Uhlig, CEO Polygon Entertainment

"Elisabeth and her book embody how my mother raised me with understanding of *the joy of giving of ourselves* as the root of true happiness." — H.R.H. Crown Princess Katherine

ELISABETH THIERIOT

DEDICATION

This book is dedicated to anyone who has ever doubted their own inner beauty and has been faced with challenges along the way.

To my children, who have been my inspiration to succeed.

FOREWORD

Some people have a gift for seeing. Their understanding of things surpasses what is easily evident and receives additional information from the living tissue itself. Some people call them medical intuitives. Elisabeth Thieriot is one of these people.

In the course of our bodywork sessions, I have been able to validate Elisabeth's insight into her own body's healing. We see the same things. The human body is an intelligent living system. It expands, absorbs, contracts, and protects based on its perception of safety and the nourishment available in the environment. That nourishment can be in the form of touch or smell or beauty. You can talk to the body in many ways, and it will listen and change according to the influences placed upon it. That's the body's job: to constantly adapt to the influences of environment. The skin is a primary agent in this process.

Elisabeth's personal discovery of the sensibility of the skin and the desirability of nourishing it, with attention to the larger seasonal moods of the environment was arrived at through observation and experimentation, following the intuition of her need for self-care. I was surprised to hear she was completely unaware of the entire tome that appeared many years ago on a similar approach to diet, written by Dr. Elson Haas, Staying Healthy with the Seasons. Elisabeth and Dr. Haas had arrived at the same conclusion, the need for seasonal changes in the care of the body.

You have no doubt heard it said that "beauty comes from within." This statement speaks, in part, to the reality that lack of stress and internal health give a glow and radiance to the skin. Stress of any kind affects multiple internal systems. Even the stress of physical disorganization, such as that following an accident, can be so costly on our energy resources that when it persists over many years, it causes a drain on the sense of vitality, possible digestive disturbances affecting nutritional intake, and compromises in immunity and cellular metabolism. This cascade of inefficiencies can result in multisystem breakdowns. Our medical system treats these things as separate symptoms. It is my observation that most multisystem breakdowns begin with shock, trauma, and physical and functional stress. However, that can be avoided through greater knowledge and understanding of how to restore balance once it's been compromised.

Elisabeth lives life to the fullest and is a glorious example of embodied knowledge. Elisabeth's seasonal concepts define her,

her family, her home, her exercise routine, and an essential healthy attitude and diet. It has been an honor to watch her at work in the world. One look at Elisabeth and you will know she walks her talk.

Commit yourself to reading and enjoying her book *Be Fabulous at Any Age: Creating Ageless Skin Through Seasonal Living*. Set your personal goals, and start on the path to bring outstanding results to your life and health, too.

— Jocelyn Olivier, CMT, MBW

Jocelyn Olivier is one of those rare individuals who has had the focus, courage, and years of experience to turn her gift into a body of knowledge for the education and treatment of others. Olivier is the founder and director of **Alive & Well! Institute of Conscious BodyWork®** (founded 1987) and **Healus Neuro Rehab Center**, both in Mill Valley, CA. She has dedicated 39 years to the development and refinement of **ConsciousBodyWork®** and **NeuroMuscularReprogramming®** (NMR). Integrating massage with muscle testing, structural balancing, and emotional-energetic resolution, and the reduction of stressshock and trauma, Ms. Olivier created a highly effective and detailed approach to the resolution of physical structural problems, even with those who have not responded previously to therapy. Through her study of neuromuscular re-education, educational kinesiology, Native American and Hawaiian Shamanism, and Chinese physical therapy (called Tui Na), Olivier created a new form of NMR.

Seeing an evolution of somatic knowledge through the communication between individual modalities, Olivier founded the **Association for Humanistic Psychology (AHP) Somatics and Wellness Community** in 1990. This organization recognizes the importance of expanding our knowledge about the human body and works to build a more integrated concept of the human body than that generated by isolated, specialized approaches. During her year as president of AHP, she raised the capital for, directed, and produced the 1999 International Somatic Congress: Body Wisdom—the culmination of a decade of work as one of the finest conferences produced in the field of somatics.

Jocelyn Olivier is the founder of **Healus Neuro Rehab Center**

Mill Valley, Calif.

For more information, visit *www.healus.com*.

TABLE OF CONTENTS

BE FABULOUS AT ANY AGE:

CREATING AGELESS SKIN THROUGH SEASONAL LIVING

Endorsements 5

Dedication 7

Foreword 8

Introduction 25

Chapter One Seasonal Living

What Is Seasonal Living? 37

What Is Seasonal Health? 39

How Do We Measure Our Health? 39

Taking Responsibility for Healing Ourselves 40

Universal Consciousness 43

Influential Philosophers and Thinkers 45

Returning to Our Natural Biological Clock 49

Skin/Body Cycles 52

Quality of Life 54

The Law of Cycles 55

Seasonal Living, Seasonal Health 57

Chapter Two Your Skin Is Your Social Calling Card

Beauty Starts With Our Health 63

Our Skin Speaks to Us and to the World 63

Supporting Natural Skin Functions 65

Natural Care for the Skin 67

Proper Balance for the Skin 68

Physical Manifestations of Toxins in the Body 71

It Is Never Too Late 72

Sunscreens 73

Noticing Our Body and Skin's Seasonal Reactions 77

Reactions to Topicals 79

Primary Loss 81

My Beauty Regimen for Ageless Skin 83

Seasonal Skin Care Tips 87

Replete™ Seasonal Skincare 89

Replete Seasonal Skincare Products 90

Chapter Three Our Six Senses

Heart, Visual, Sound, Smell, Touch and Taste 103

Our Senses and Their Corresponding Body/Exercise/

Art References 106

Hierarchic Relationship between Two Principles ...107

Support from the Heart 107

Importance of Touch 112

Overstimulation Affects Us 113

Sensory Balancers 116

Importance of Music and Other Arts 121

Chapter Four Our Physical Health

We Only Have One Body 125

Experience No Fatigue 126

Six Sense Needs for Different Nutrients 127

Give Your Body a Break Every Week 128

Our Breath Is Movement 128

Neuromuscular Reset 132

Seasonal Activities and Exercise 133

Seasonal Feel-Fabulous Choices 135

Chapter Five Exercise

Walking 137

Yoga 139

Other Types of Exercise 140

Chapter Six Our Emotional Health

Digesting Emotions 147

Emotional Retention 150

Love Aspect 151

What We Wear Affects Our Emotional State of Mind ..153

Meditation, the Controlled Breath 155

When I End My Day 156

The Law of Opposites 156

One Minute of Introspection 157

Chapter Seven Renewal and Repair: The Essential Value of Sleep

Treat Your Bed and Your Sheets Like a Sanctuary for

Your Body and Your Sleep 161

We Repair During Sleep 161

The Work of the Unconscious 164

Circadian Rhythm 165

Lack of Sleep Can Cause Toxicity 166

Sleep Aids 166

Burn Fat While You Sleep 169

SAD (Seasonal Affective Disorder) 169

Internal Organs Function on a Biological Clock 170

Cyclical Rhythms 175

The Cycle of 23 177

Chapter Eight Seasonal Eating

Digestion 182

Meal Time 183

Emotional Effect on Digestion 185

Food Combinations 185

Corresponding Fruits and Vegetables to Our Organ

Needs 188

You Can Rebuild Your DNA by Supplementing with

Trace Nutrients 189

Proteins 192

Carbohydrates 192

Fats 194

Herbs 195

Seasonal Digestive Aids 196

Chapter Nine Seasonal Food

Our Food, the Seasonal Antidote 199

Food Is Medicine 201

Beneficial Herbs and Plants 205

Climate Influence and Grain Consumption 216

Our Bodies Process Foods According to Seasonal

States 216

Our Food Attractions Match the Seasons 219

Seasonal Food Preparations 222

Chapter Ten Supplements

Seasonal Supplement Suggestions 227

Benefits of Supplements 230

Overlooked (but necessary) Supplements 240

Mayan Periodic Chart of the Elements 242

Chapter Eleven Water, The Elixir Of Life

Our Cell Membranes 247

Signs You Need Water 248

The Fountain of Youth 250

Nutrients in Water 252

Why Ocean Water Is Different 254

Trace Minerals 254

Chapter Twelve Embracing Change

Intelligent Choices 260

Happiness Is a Choice—Choose It 260

Courage Comes From Willpower Rooted in Faith ..262

Making a Contract 266

Understanding Our Habits and Practices Reduces

Stress and Aging 267

Hierarchy of Our Existence 269

Improvement—Focus On Fabulous Living Through

Feelings and Beliefs 270

Reinforcement 272

Giving Back—Joy Makes You Younger 274

Our Time 276

Travel in Comfort 277

Chapter Thirteen Harmonizing Your Living Space

Constructing Your World 281

Our Home 281

Sensual Smells 282

Organizing Your Work Environment 284

The Value of Gardens 285

Let the Vivid Colors of Flowers Brighten Your Day ...289

Our Purchases and Decisions 290

Beautiful Living That Echoes the Seasons 290

Chapter Fourteen Seasonal Personal Fashion

Fashion & Style 297

Women's Shoes 300

Men's Shoes 301

Gemstones 303

Chapter Fifteen Seasonal Travel

Seasonal Travel: Travel Destinations 311

Chapter Sixteen Seasonal Living for Ageless Beauty

Ageless Longevity 321

Find and Develop Seasonal Activities 322

Art 323

Introducing the Family to Nature 325

Taking Time for Seeing Friends and Having Pets ..327

Farewell 330

Appendix A 334

Appendix B 345

Appendix C 352

Bibliography/Resources 356

Index 359

Acknowledgements 364

Special Thanks 365

ELISABETH THIERIOT

Another Spring

By g woodruff

She belongs to the elegance
   of another time.
A sweet elixir seduces
   whenever she speaks.

She wields her wand gently
with the mastery that comes
   not from practice
   but from birth.

Once upon a time
             shifted
and built her a castle
to protect her from
the awkwardness of
             surprise.
But even more from
the threat that
   her soul,
     her wealth,

her beauty
could so easily become plunder
for the unworthy barbarians
who stalked her
forests and fertile vineyards.

The Barbarian Prince sees her
from across the verdant fields
gliding effortlessly.
April breezes
blowing the violet silk she wears
that never touches
her ivory skin.

The Princess walks the stone ramparts
    tending lovingly to her domain.
She alone plants
    the magic seed that feeds
her grateful wards
secure, transcendent, reveling
within this fleeting mist.

The Prince, his men and horses
    clad in iron and leather,

compact the earth
  with some thunder
    as He approaches.

With shimmering steel drawn
and a bow designed to conquer
  the sternest foe,
He is constrained now
to pursue this priceless vision.

The smell of lavender
gentle laughter,
slippers tapping the stone steps
sounds serene, magnify the silence

  even the rustling of her gown
    screams
above the faint flutter of
a thousand butterflies.

As he thinks to speak,
  She and all her castle
slip away into the morning mist,

but not without
leaving him a string
of wild flowers
   to hang about his sheath
confiding in the softest tones
   "Not now my love.
      Maybe another time;
         another spring."

Photo by Ashley Farrah Horowitz

INTRODUCTION

I wrote *Be Fabulous At Any Age: Creating Ageless Skin Through Seasonal Living* in order to share the life-changing lessons I have learned about health and well-being. The system I have devised is a natural, long-term solution to problems for which Western medicine still has no real cure. On my journey toward physical and emotional health, I have learned that patience, faith, consistency, and stamina cannot be bought from a pharmacy, and that gentle methods and applications are most successful for maintaining a balanced system. We truly are what we eat…and what we believe in. Both have a tremendous effect on who we are, our habits, and how we treat our skin. The environment we create both emotionally and physically supports who we ultimately become.

As a child, I experienced a wonderful, fulfilling family life. We lived in harmony with each other and with the changing seasons.

Our activities included skiing and ice-skating in the winter. In the spring we played tennis, went horseback riding, and hiking. During the summer we enjoyed seaside relaxation, ocean swims, volleyball and badminton competitions, and rock climbing in the mountains.

In autumn, we would hunt and hike, play table tennis, bridge, and other card games, and attend the opera, symphony, and ballet.

There was a very distinct separation between the seasons themselves. Each one represented a time to rest and a time to produce, a time to recover and time to gear up, logical harmony and rhythm, predictability, and expectations.

My family's unspoken expectation was to be proactive and to perform according to these rhythms. This would prepare us for life taking its course, whether planned or unexpected. In late summer, we would work together to prepare the winter preserves, which was always a happy and memorable ritual for us. We would spend weekends conserving fruits, pickling meats, cucumbers, and other vegetables. We knew each jar so intimately that when it was served later that year, we would announce the proud creator.

Food preparation for the winter was a wonderful tradition filled with laughter, storytelling, a sense of accomplishment, and renewed self-esteem. It taught us how important it is to plan from season to season in order for our lives to be enriched and cared for in a proactive way. It taught us the true value of timing, gave us a sense of passing opportunities, and instilled in us the importance of readiness for whatever may come next.

My family remains close, despite our geographic distances. We live on separate continents, but continue to plan and get together for seasonal activities.

During my puberty, through my encounters with a series of less-than-comfortable new body symptoms, I hoped blindly for a fix from Western medicine. I soon discovered that the change in my body's chemistry from that of a girl to a woman required changes in lifestyle that included my sleep regime, food choices, and exercise routine.

Even though I grew up in a nurturing and supportive environment, I was faced with many challenges when I entered puberty. At the age of 15, with excruciating sinus problems, I was exposed to the solutions of Western medicine. Due to misdiagnosed sinus issues resulting from a feather allergy, doctors performed surgery; they later did another in order to remove my appendix as a cure for food poisoning. A third surgery resulted from the fact that as a child, I consumed a quart of heavy cream each night to maintain my weight. With the onset of puberty and the resulting increased hormonal activity, my glands became over stimulated, causing my ovaries to over-produce female hormones. The Western medicine cure was to perform yet another surgery.

Following that, I was prescribed a contraceptive pill to control the ovaries' production, which caused breast lumps within two months. The doctors wanted to operate again, and I was told that I might never have children. At this point, I lost all trust in Western medicine. I halted all prescriptions and tests. I learned the value of natural balance, implemented it into my daily life, and within three months, I was free of all problems and symptoms, and still, I remain in great health.

My issues with modern medicine are all too common. There is an enthusiasm for cutting and removing parts as a cure, in addition to over-prescribing medications. The patients and their doctors who are eager to please with quick results are probably fulfilling the current need for instant gratification. The doctors were treating my symptoms, not their causes, in order to deliver on unnatural expectations. My body was simply doing what it was supposed to be doing. My health issues resolved with simple fixes; all I needed to do was stop drinking the heavy cream. In addition, I figured out the simple act of ridding my bedroom of down comforters and pillows helped to eliminate my sinus irritations. Even at this young age, I learned that understanding and respecting my own body signals and energy resources was needed to get through a busy day. I came to see that rest is necessary, and working 18 or 20 hours a day will make even a young person sick.

I received hard lessons by undergoing one unnecessary surgery after another. Instead of treating the underlying causes of my issues, the doctors simply treated my symptoms without giving me directions to prevent the same issues from happening again. This led me to develop a deep belief that my health is dependent on my own clear thinking, research, and an understanding of what is going on with my own body and my family's health.

I vowed to keep my family and myself healthy at an optimum level and prepare them for self-care by teaching them that this was their own responsibility. Although my personal experiences began my journey of self-healing, it was growing up on daily fresh vegetable juices and freshly cooked, chemical-free, and natural food that sparked my understanding that what we eat affects how we look and feel.

When I was pregnant for the first time with my son, the hormonal and physiological changes throughout my body made me more sensitive to the scents of cosmetics I was using and caused such bad skin reactions that I had to change brands. It was obvious to me that what goes on in our body manifests itself through our skin. When a skin condition appeared after the birth of my daughter, I reached out to a variety of doctors and was eventually invited to a 50-doctor symposium at New York University as a *mystery condition* patient. They began a series of tests, and each one showed a copper carrier deficiency, which they wanted to treat with steroid cream and plastic surgery for aesthetic improvement.

I rejected their quick-fix suggestions and decided to focus on working with an open-minded general physician who also believed in alternative medicine. I was prescribed a 10-month course of antibiotics that eliminated the fallout from the imbalance created in my body. It was not quick or easy.

Once the course of medication was completed, I halted the process of destruction and began to create a process of rebuilding. The journey to repair my skin from that damage took seven years. By using herbs and botanicals to create a full reconstruction of my skin's integrity, I successfully designed a cocktail of minerals, herbs, and vitamins. In addition to skin exfoliation and exercise, I fully adapted my philosophy of seasonal living as a building block for my system's recovery; I finally saw it all come together, and I started achieving results. I attained my goal: bringing my body back into balance without creating extreme conditions was the key. The result is that after looking like a burn victim for years, I am free of all blemishes and have since recovered completely with a combination of healing herbs, natural botanical serums, self-care, and seasonal living as my choice for a healthy lifestyle.

In my 20s, in an effort to save my husband from cancer, I became very interested in Macrobiotics. These studies opened my eyes to the effects of a mother's diet on her unborn child (I was pregnant at the time with my second child). I found it fascinating.

My journey during this difficult period of my husband's illness was both rewarding and painful. He eventually made a full recovery. Having lived through this process of discovery, I am happy to help you implement my philosophy of health and well-being into your life to achieve better health and ageless longevity.

Sight, sound, smell, touch, taste, and emotional feelings are our receptors to the outside world. They determine what we like to eat, our intellect, characteristics, energy levels, and mental capabilities; all of these are very important in the daily rhythm that is supportive of our own biological clock.

Incorporating all I have learned, I now know how to balance my body's needs, and I am now enjoying a healthy life with my two wonderful children.

I look back in horror at the consequences that could have resulted had I listened to the advice of medical doctors who wanted to cure my skin's underlying systemic problems with surface-stretching plastic surgery. I am relieved to know that I have avoided yet another intrusion, especially one that would not have cured my problem. Even so, there are circumstances where plastic surgery is needed to restore an original contour or for corrective reasons. The key is to maintain and recreate the strength and texture of youthful skin through the restoration of our cells' integrity and strength and prevention of their premature breakdown.

In truth, we can only make decisions from within the boundaries of the knowledge that we possess. I am thankful that I had the sense to walk away from the doctor's advice and follow my intuition and acquire more knowledge. I am still amazed that it took me 10 years to shake the social pressure of listening to Western medical opinions as the only reference point.

Sometimes we fail to notice that the most obvious things we are doing in our own behaviors and consumptions are the cause of our problems. We focus on symptoms, rather than causes, because that is what we are conditioned to do. I urge you to be more mindful and inquisitive about what throws you off balance and inhibits your optimal health. This may spare you a few trips to the doctor, surgeries, and any number of ailments. Modern medicine saves lives and natural seasonal living creates the best quality of life. Listen to your body; listen to your own advice. No one knows your body like you do.

Today, thankfully, many physicians have come to the realization that they need to provide *total* treatment. Doctors are asking patients questions concerning their emotional state, environmental conditions at work and at home, education, socio-economic status, and other factors that may contribute to their symptoms. We are hopefully on our way to creating a collective collaboration between Western medicine and Eastern philosophies concerning the body's state of health and mind.

Observing and understanding individual lives is so important for doctors. They should partner with a patient on the road to healing. Pharmaceutical companies have always relied on botanicals in their production of medicines. Even now, after years of research, cosmetic companies are turning to nature for its ability to heal and restore the skin. My skincare line **Replete**™ is based entirely on natural resources. I have combined the best of nature with the best of today's technology.

Nature may take longer, but the solution is permanent. Many of us seek the pleasure of instant gratification. I find that setting a reasonable expectation helps to set the timeline.

As I began to acknowledge the need for natural skin care, I realized that the only two obstacles are knowing what we need and having the ability to acquire it. That realization led me to create my own skincare line to gain accessibility. I looked to Hawaii, Africa, India, and other mineral-rich parts of the world in search of nutrients for my **Replete**™ skincare line. I have reached out and communicated with healers to find the most rare and clinically-proven botanicals that defy age. I discovered that most precious healing plant properties were passed on from generation of healers

INTRODUCTION

to generation of healers... *until now.*

We must learn to listen to our inner voice first and recognize the process of accessing it. The first step of self-preservation is the willingness to look and learn from the past, then add the new and the unknown. If you are experiencing doubt, use that as a signal that you need to further educate yourself and fully understand whatever that may be.

Elisabeth Thieriot

We are our life's managers, and we create the

quality of our journey through life from the information

we have and choices we make in the process of living our

lives. Our journey provides us with the reference library

which we need to use to create a successful life.

Photo by Cindy Shelton

CHAPTER ONE

SEASONAL LIVING

September is my most favorite time of the year. No matter where I go in the world, I am greeted with the distinctive fragrance of autumn in the air. Harvest time is coming to completion, and cities are pulsing with new energy for the business season. I love the sense of closure that autumn brings after playful summer relaxation as we move into a more intellectual, introspective, and highly productive time of the year.

What is Seasonal Living?

Seasonal living is a whole new way of looking at the quality of your life, staying fabulous, and having ageless skin. Seasonal living will help you in the process of making decisions about how you want to feel on a daily basis. You'll understand the interdependence between what you put into your body and onto your skin and how you spend your time and precious resources. When you align yourself with seasonal living by following the cycles of nature and how they affect the body, you will come to love and appreciate your healthy lifestyle change. You will realize that timing is everything.

My own condition of undiagnosed illness motivated me to look for solutions outside Western medicine early on. When I did not have information, I relied on others who seemed to have more information to guide me to the right outcome, but they did not. Going back to nature for ageless longevity and following my seasonal clock has made me healthier in every sense of the word.

The practice of seasonal living encourages the body's natural ability to heal itself through personal attention, chemical-free, natural foods, and nutritional support, and through the completion of biological cycles. When the body is free of chemicals and excesses, it releases itself from burdens and can therefore heal. Become part of the cycle of life by implementing this into your lifestyle to live longer, healthier, and more energetically. The quality of your life can then extend as time goes by.

Sadly, a good example of the impact seasonal living has on our lives is that of milking cows that are deprived of seasonal living and are only barn kept. They showed a short lifespan of only three years, in comparison to free range milking cows living productively for 10-13 years.

In *Be Fabulous At Any Age: Creating Ageless Skin Through*

Seasonal Living, I will share with you some of my experiences, beliefs, and studies of self-care, including skin, diet, sleep, mental and physical regimens, and lifestyle choices. Total beauty starts with balance between your physical, spiritual, and emotional state; their interconnections are what create ageless, beautiful skin and vitality. There must be synchronization on all three levels of mind, body, and spirit for complete beauty to manifest. There is no other way.

What is Seasonal Health?

The cycles that govern the world in which we live and the universe, as far as we know it, are undeniable. Seasonal health is a function of paying attention to the changes in the seasons and transitioning our lives along with them. Along with my own research, I have combined my experiences and discoveries to share optimal health with you. This is a journey into total health in every sense of the word. Seasonal health is about living in balance and supporting our system through seasonal changes.

How Do We Measure Our Health?

Signs of Optimal Health

Skin, the Message Board of Health = Normal & Radiant

Energy Level = Energy Available on Demand

Balanced Gland System = No Cravings

Reparative Deep Sleep = Waking Up Rested

Balanced Mind = Positive Outlook = Positive Outcome

Long & Short-Term Memory = Both Easy to Recall & Vivid

Clarity of Ethics = Internal Peace = Alignment with our Intentions

Ideal Body Weight = Balance between Mind, Body & Soul

Taking Responsibility for Healing Ourselves

In practice, seasonal living encourages the body's natural ability to heal itself through personal attention and nutritional support. When we make the commitment to free our bodies of chemical additives, we heal more quickly and with better efficiency.

In our youth, we are prone to adventure, love, and experience all that life has to offer. Your lifestyle is your choice, and seasonal living provides the best that nature can offer as we go through life. When we pay attention to the effects of how we treat ourselves and how we live, the result is freedom from fear and a new sense of well-being that spreads to all with whom we come in contact. As you implement this philosophy into your lifestyle and make it a practice, you will live a longer, healthier and more energetic life. When you move with the cycle of life, the quality of your life will extend your age.

I believe that our intentions affect
everything we do and everyone we know.

Macrobiotics has made a significant impact on my life and that of my family. The word "macro" means "great" and "bios" refers to "life." Addressing the needs of both is the way to receive the most out of life in an effortless flow from nature. I follow the macrobiotic principal and food selection with the addition of some proteins, and I adhere to the principles that govern the practical application of the natural laws of change, balance, and cycles.

The most important guiding principles are:

- ❖ Principle of opposites for balance
- ❖ Four-season climate living
- ❖ Consumption of natural produce, grown within your hemisphere (Northern or Southern)
- ❖ Food combining

Opposite tendency functions are:

- ❖ Expansion to contraction
- ❖ Diffusion to fusion
- ❖ Dispersion to assimilation
- ❖ Separation to gathering
- ❖ Decomposition to organization
- ❖ Hibernation to exuberance

For more on the guidelines and foods for seasonal living, please see Appendix A.

The same principles of opposites apply to foods from sweets to salty, from dense to fluid to gas. This applies to everything we do: how the world operates around us, how we prepare food, how our emotional state is, and how the seasons transition from one extreme to another. Seasonal living is about applying these philosophies to our lives in an updated, timely fashion. The body needs essential nutrients to function efficiently as it removes excesses and toxins. Our body continually adjusts its needs to its own timed processes in a changing environment. When we create a balance between what we put on our skin, what we put in our body, and how we live, we can then adjust to changes in a peaceful manner, thus creating ageless longevity and skin that stays youthful and resilient.

Universal Consciousness

Consciousness is the interpreter of all intentions.

Human consciousness is our first source of information after our awareness brings attention to it. It informs us of intentions before we experience them through our senses. Intentions reach into the smallest particles and cells, giving them purpose.

Our degree of consciousness is based on our awareness. Some refer to this combination as one's IQ. We also know that through continuous study, our mind expands and increases our IQ. This then represents a greater level of awareness, leading to greater consciousness and allowing us to be more accurate in interpreting the intentions we come in contact with or our self-created ones.

Our intentions decide who we ultimately are. Intention is what runs the world as we know it. It makes us who we are, and it puts everything into motion.

Action→Reaction→Outcome

There is an ancient book called *The I-Ching (The Book of Change)*, which describes how intention works and which of them are appropriate or not. This leads to one's developing positive or negative outcomes. I call this the DNA of Intentions, which perfectly parallels the 64 codes of our DNA.

Without intent, there is no action/reaction

Without intent, there is absence of value - 0 and motion

It is my hope to show you how your self-care and awareness will lead you to a life that is full of health, vitality, and beauty for ageless longevity. You can feel fabulous at any age! Sharing my vision and the universal consciousness of how the cycles, seasons, foods, our bodies' functions, and the rhythms going on around us govern everything we do will give you insight into ageless longevity and natural beauty.

Seasonal Tip:

Having a hunch is part of receiving information. A hunch is part of connecting to the universal consciousness and receiving information from it. When you have a hunch, follow it; do not dismiss it. Most mistakes are made when we think of a hunch as not valid enough to act upon.

Influential Philosophers and Thinkers

My seasonal living philosophy includes some elements of Macrobiotics from my studies with Michio Kushi, along with information I gathered and practiced from my childhood upbringing that was influenced by people like Edgar Cayce, Rudolf Steiner, Robert Ballard, and many others.

Michio Kushi was a student of George Ohsawa, the founder of Macrobiotics. Ohsawa lived from 1893 until 1966 and began his quest for health at the age of 19 when he was diagnosed with tuberculosis. In an effort to save himself, he set his mind and resources to overcoming tuberculosis. He was able to cure himself and devoted his life to teaching macrobiotic science, incorporating science, ethics, religion, and philosophy from the macrobiotic and seasonal living perspectives. Kushi is responsible for introducing Macrobiotics to the United States. I sought him out in the last trimester of my second pregnancy when my husband was diagnosed with cancer. I did not want my children to grow up without their father.

My studies with Kushi affected my family's health in a positive and profound way. I was not completely unfamiliar with the concept of healing foods, since I also had tuberculosis at the age of five that went undiagnosed until I was seven. By then, I was fully healed through good nutrition, and only faint signs of it were left.

In the course of my research, I also discovered Edgar Cayce. Cayce's method of communication about health problems and the belief about having a sense of personal responsibility for your own health may have been unorthodox at the time, but his results were indisputable. Cayce's readings were widespread, from skin diseases to diet, cancer, and mental illness. My particular interests included vitality of the skin, childbirth, healing, and how vitamin deficiencies impact our body and mind. Many of his recommendations have proven to be accurate, working as promised. Incorporating many natural remedies, Cayce's ideas also included the connection between body muscles and bone alignments and structures, all influenced by our state of awareness. Cayce saw optimal health as a holistic and natural process. This resonates with my past and the treatment of my symptoms, rather than my illnesses.

Rudolf Steiner, a philosopher, social reformer, and esoteric, further influenced me. Mr. Steiner founded the Waldorf School in Germany and introduced his unique approach to education. My daughter was fortunate to attend two of over a thousand Waldorf schools worldwide, one in San Francisco and one in Heidelberg, Germany. The Waldorf cultural philosophy is called anthroposophy, which is related to the inner development of perception, imagination, and intuition in a very natural, scientific sense through movement and behaviors. The connection between our physiological and internal spiritual needs resonated with my beliefs. Steiner was a pioneer when it came to education, farming, medicine, ethics, and many other areas. I find it fascinating how these correlate. A good example is the link between learning development by using body proportions as guidelines for successful assimilations of information and overall readiness to handle tasks. The process of connecting our inner and outer needs for optimal health is what I have found to work best; this is also the missing element in current living practices.

Another contributor to my point of view was Dr. Robert Ballard. Through his deep-sea adventures, he was able to bring us an understanding of the world under the sea and have it shed light on optimal health. He was one of the first to reveal that life can thrive under the sea in unique and adverse conditions. In areas of the ocean where there is intense pressure and temperatures, deep-sea vents are teeming with life. A worldwide educator, Ballard founded the Institute for Exploration. His discovery of the restorative qualities of the ocean water off the coast of Maui has influenced me to use it for its healing properties. Sourced from 3,000 feet below the surface of the ocean and being 2,000 years old, this seawater contains undisturbed nutrients and has everything needed to produce new and healthy cells in the body. More notably, the attributes of this seawater closely approximate of the gestation period in the womb. I use this water daily to create balance in my own body and have incorporated it in my **Replete Aqua**™ and seasonal skin care formulas for the benefit of everyone.

When I studied with Michio Kushi, and learned of natural

healing methods, I also discovered how the creation of our bodies, from the arches of our feet to our hands, ears, and facial features, are also representative of the current state of our internal organs. Our organs are affected by what goes into our system. *We are what we eat.* What we come in contact with has an effect on our entire being. By focusing on physical features, it is possible to understand many things about a person, their past, their diet, their family, their self-care, and their habits. This comprises knowing their current needs. Our features change as part of a response to our deficiencies, just as they change with our intellectual stimulus and conscious evolvement. Needing minerals or other nutrients is often displayed as illness, marked as a side effect of medication or minor symptomatic discomforts. This is why replenishing them is so important, and maintaining our mineral and vitamin balance preserves the beauty and quality of life.

Returning To Our Natural Biological Clock

Getting into balance with nature is the key, and this is just the beginning. The balance in the body is constantly changing as it reacts to the food we eat, the seasons, aging, situations in one's life aggravated by stress, and all other aspects of our day-to-day activities. Many different factors affect our overall condition: the rate of our pulse, being introverted or extroverted, thinking of the past or future, engaging in mental or physical activities. What matters is that we recognize our traits and live with them. Men and women each possess traits of the opposite sex and should adjust to the balances of their food consumption in relation to their gender and needs. It is an ongoing aspect of our human condition. Seasonal living seeks to ease the transitions as we move between the oppositional physical and emotional states.

It is also important to notice how our innate state mirrors nature. For example, women and men experience cycles. Both the fertility cycle and seasons are governed by the laws of nature.

Fertility cycles of men and women are well documented by birth records as well as clinical studies:

- ❖ Winter is the quiet fertile time of our cycles for both sexes. It is a good time to conceive, hibernate, relax, and enjoy this quiet time with family.

- ❖ Spring is the beginning time of expansion and the most natural time to grow with new life.

- ❖ Summer is when your body is in the perfect state of

full expansion. It is perfect for the late stage of pregnancy, and it is the lowest point of fertility for both sexes.

❖ Autumn is the optimal time to deliver new life, as our bodies are starting to contract with the changing seasons.

SKIN/BODY CYCLES

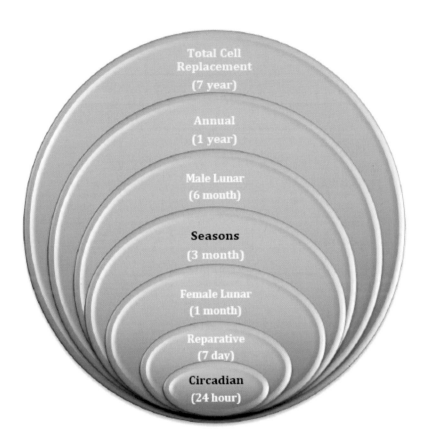

Skin cycles explained:

1. Total Cell Renewal: Every seven years, our body fully completes a total cell renewal, whereby all cells are new as compared to the cells of the body seven years ago.

2. Annual: Every year, our skin completes the seasonal cycles. Not properly completing this cycle can be damaging to the skin.

3. Male Lunar: Every six months, the male undergoes a hormonal lunar cycle.

4. Seasons: Every season, our skin undergoes a different hemispheric cycle. Accordingly, there are four cycles: Winter, Spring, Summer, and Autumn.

5. Female Lunar: Every month, women go through a lunar cycle.

6. Reparative: Every seven days, our skin completes a reparative cycle.

7. Circadian: Every day, our skin undergoes a complete circadian cycle: a day defense, assimilation and production of nutrients from light and night repair, detox, and replacement cycle.

Seasonal Tip:

Red clover, ginger tea, and raspberry leaf extract are wonderful tonics that help you adjust to your body's changing needs.

Quality Of Life

Your quality of life is directly related to how you choose to spend your time and what you put on or into your body: food, medicine, cosmetics, and even emotions. Spend your time enjoying and participating in your life by making decisions that resonate positively with your health. The idea is to create a very simple self-care program that focuses on a clean and natural life. This doesn't mean you can't have a glass of wine at dinner or you should restrict yourself from what gives you enjoyment. In fact, it is just the opposite. When you consistently and regularly pay attention to what you put into your body and onto your skin, you will soon realize the long-term benefits. This will even allow you to indulge once in a while—when you make a conscious decision to do so—without paying a high price for it. Be proactive and plan a skin care routine; it only takes a nominal amount of time to replenish the daily loss of nutrients from travel or stress. Educate yourself and supplement your diet with vitamins and minerals. Your environment is extremely important to your well-being. Pay attention to your surroundings; discover an atmosphere that works well for you and your emotional and physical state of mind, and then take time to appreciate it. Gratitude is part of having a full experience in life.

Many of us have strayed from being present front-and-center in our lives. The time that we spend in our homes should truly be a time of comfort, rejuvenation, calmness, and happiness. When you come home, you repair by rebalancing through your sleep, caring for your skin, taking nutrients, and rebalancing emotionally through your surroundings. Your home is your temple and must be of the best quality you can provide for yourself and your family.

The Law of Cycles

All that we know to exist is subject to cyclic laws: all that surrounds us and affects us, whether you see it, feel it, hear it, or know it. Layered laws of cycles and their order rule us all. Everything has its own vibration and its own specific rhythm, whether it is the earth on its axis, the life cycle of a seed, seasonal changes during the year, a human reproductive cycle, or life in the sea or underneath the earth's surface. All of these are part of our world. We know everything is interlinked in perfect harmony. We call it an ecosystem and know that if just one part is lost, the balance is lost too. We, as humans, have our own cycles. We have the senses to feel, to love, to learn, to mature our understanding, and to contribute to the betterment of our society. We can then better decide how we want to fit into the cultural and social part of our life cycle. Our intentions will pave the way for how we will experience the journey: our actions will create reactions to those intentions, and our awareness will guide us through the maze of enfolding events.

As we decide on our intentions, one situation at a time, we will determine our fate and we will establish our ultimate destiny. We all have our own natural cycles that are personal to us, based on our place of birth, our path of environmental impact, and, partially, our DNA. When we work in harmony with our natural cycles by giving awareness to the other layered cycles occurring around us, the likelihood of succeeding is greatest. When we decide to swim upstream, battling and forcing our wills against the natural currents that have clearly presented us with the signs to change direction, it will usually end in failure. Our tendency to diminish or ignore the unknown—whether we don't understand it or simply choose to ignore it—is counterproductive and sabotaging to life's natural progress. Refuting logical support for the existence of new information directly undermines your own life's success. It is always easier to fight the probability of a rhythm if it conflicts with your own practice and quality of life at the moment, especially when you don't see the immediate benefit stemming from it. Recognize the different ways in which a select few, in the strangest of circumstances, managed to have ongoing luck and seem to know what others do not. They are generally seen simply as highly successful people. This does not occur by chance, but the way they go through life; it results from following the path that was presented to them instead of forcing their way on others or against circumstances. They understood that, for them, behaving this way was their path to advancement and success. You, too, can become the master of your destiny.

Being present in our environment and noticing what the earth has brought to us and using it is part of tuning in. Once we do, we will automatically begin to care for ourselves better. This is true beauty, and it only occurs when you're on a transcendent plane of high awareness, completely present in the moment. Your confidence increases and you are no longer in fear or wonder of what will happen next. You are then *in-the-know*. The present and future become one because you are mentally, emotionally, and physically aware of a link between them.

I describe this as "action and reaction" = outcome.

Seasonal Living, Seasonal Health

In order for you to evolve as a complete person, you must first assess and accept your starting point with full honesty. Only then can you proceed to develop your physical, emotional, and spiritual maturity.

❖ **Spring** – Focus on detoxing your body, clearing your house of clutter, and ridding your house of winter dust from heating systems and tracked-in mud. Think about a healthy diet alternative. One day a week, try a vegetable broth fast from noon to noon for a 24-hour period throughout the entire spring season. Make your vegetable broth by simmering seasonal fresh, leafy green vegetables at a very low temperature, then, strain them to retain as much of the liquid as possible. Add sea salt for flavor, while boosting the mineral content.

❖ **Summer** – With summer comes heat and open windows. Change sheets and winter bedding to light-weight fabrics to avoid overheating in the summer months and allow the skin to breathe freely. Exercise and enjoy the outdoors, connect with friends, and enjoy the bounty of summer fruits and vegetables. Focus on a diet of fruits, raw salads, watermelon (an enzymatic cleanser and internal body rinser), and fresh clean foods. Avoid the intake of fatty and greasy foods during the summer. Get plenty of sun exposure to accumulate reserves of Vitamin D for bodily functions and other self-produced elements need for the upcoming long winter months. To avoid burning your skin, begin by gradually exposing it to the sun for as little as 20 minutes a day after 3 p.m. For extended periods outdoors, wear a hat and cotton or linen to protect the skin.

❖ **Autumn** – Begin to collect your thoughts and turn them inward in mental and physical preparation for accumulating and storing nutrients in your body for the winter. Gather all the intellectual information from the past nine months so you can start the study or work cycle and prepare to spend more time indoors. Eat seasonal vegetables rich in vitamins and minerals; you can identify them by their rich deep colors. During the autumn months, your body prepares for the mineral deficient winter months and will readily store everything you come in contact with and eat. Ensuring chemical-free environments and foods is of the utmost importance during autumn. All the toxins you acquire during this time will be released into your system during the winter months, causing skin problems.

❖ **Winter** – Secure your home against the elements and create space for indoor family activities. Change the environment into deeper, richer colors, warmer, thicker fabrics, and proper lighting in the study area. Regulate your clock and go to bed earlier with the cycle of the sun. Consume fruit compotes as well as stews and rich foods. Enjoy grapefruit and other citrus as they are seasonal enzymatic cleansers for the skin and internal systems. Supplement with Vitamin D.

Photo by Drew Altizer

Each season should be highlighted by some form of celebration with friends and family.

Photo by Liza Gershman

CHAPTER TWO

YOUR SKIN IS YOUR SOCIAL CALLING CARD

Beauty Starts With Our Health

Healthy people are automatically more beautiful. They glow and resonate with their environments. Their beauty comes from a balance of interconnectedness with their health, spirituality, and emotional condition.

Our Skin Speaks to Us and to the World

Our skin speaks to us by how it looks and feels: its color, texture, sensitivity, softness, and how it acts. It changes according to seasonal environment, our diets, our activity, our water consumption, minerals, and what we put on it. Your skin is your largest organ and should be treated as a vital organ.

People are more and more concerned about aging and have taken great cosmetic measures to appear younger and healthier. You can reduce the aging process through proper care internally and topically with seasonal living and nutrition. The new "Med-Spa" solutions available to us now open the door to long-term assistance and ongoing treatments, but beauty does start from within. Beauty begins with our thoughts, our nutrition, our personal care, and our environment. Our expressions not only reveal our thoughts, but also organ functions represented there. When you experience negativity, it affects the Vitamin B and potassium levels in your body. If you notice deep lines appearing on your face or on your ears, cheeks or forehead, you may have an imbalance of sodium or potassium. In my seasonal formulas, I include offsets for stressors; in my life, I prepare my thoughts by focusing on the positives.

Have you ever wondered why some people have charisma and others don't? Charisma is the essence we develop within ourselves: the aura that emanates around us and shows most visibly on our skin. Every single organ of the body is represented in our face. As the head, shoulders, spinal cord, sexual organs, thighs, knees, feet, stomach, and large intestine are all associated with internal organs, they reveal their conditions on the face.

Supporting Natural Skin Functions

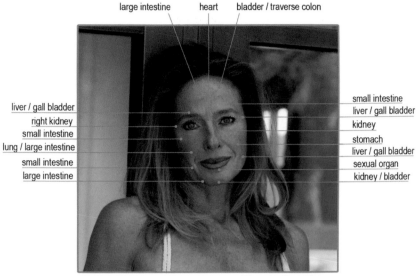

Photo by Deva Sexton

Your face is the message board of your body.

It is important to understand that you are creating a support system for bodily functions that are already ongoing. Skin absorbs anything we apply to it and carries those compounds into the blood stream. What you use has to be very gentle, non-shocking, and chemical free, and it must support optimal skin function. Over the last few years, medicine has accumulated and adopted more and more practices that involve the skin's ability to regenerate itself.

The presence of toxins in the body can manifest as skin problems.

Flaky red patches on the skin's surface may reveal an overworked or stressed liver. Red cheeks can signify stressed lungs and bronchioles. Inflamed and overly sensitive skin may be the result of parasites in the liver. Stressed and overused kidneys can cause under eye bags. This undercores that the skin is a receptor and a processor! If we put a nicotine patch on our skin to stop smoking or a patch on our skin to stop semen production or ovulation, then why would we not use topical formulas to feed and support our skin? Cosmetic brands offer chemically produced products that can be toxic and dangerous. We put them on without knowing what we are doing, blindly following the advice and promises of marketing ads and then wondering why we have undefined illnesses. The smells alone can cause headaches.

When we ask why not apply nutrients that support our needs directly to our skin, it seems clear that what we need changes seasonally. We have had thinkers and leaders giving us notice of seasonal changes, recommending seasonal harvests as a source of nutrients. So why should we not reach out to harvest the season through global resources and remove local limitations? It's time to use cosmetics and naturally formulated extracts to deliver the nutrients our bodies need to sustain optimal health. Because our skin is a living, breathing organ, it is very important that its function is not impaired. Using natural plant remedies not only beautifies the skin externally, but also creates ageless beauty by healing internally.

Natural Care for the Skin

While we think of caring for ourselves through healthy eating, shouldn't that care be extended to the other products we use? What about dental products, personal hygiene, deodorants, soaps, skin care, cosmetics, and conditioners? Is it because the list of ingredients has been made so complex that we just gloss over it? This strange behavior is costing us our health. We should consider more seriously the ramifications of cosmetics, pharmaceuticals, and medical treatments and move back towards nature and the source of the life we are part of. It is common sense, but too often, it gets lost in the speed of life.

We should avoid chemicals on our skin for the same reasons we would not eat them. Everything we apply to our skin goes into our bloodstream, so why are we applying chemicals that our bodies were not designed to process? Chemical additives can cause many reactions in our bodies and on our skin. Yet, we may not realize whether they originated from our cosmetics or our food. Chemicals in pesticides used in the late 40s to early 50s have been proven to affect the central nervous system, causing people to develop Parkinson's-like shaking and other symptoms, like weakness and nervousness.

The better choice is to become comfortable with using produce or natural foods as part of our care system. For example, an occasional facial with egg yolk and honey is a quick way to repair skin from sun and wind exposure. It can be fun being this natural—it gives us so much more to play with! Having gained the knowledge and skills to use the healing power of botanicals from all over the world, I would like to share the benefits with everyone through my skin care line.

Proper Balance for the Skin

The food we eat causes an acidic or alkaline environment for our skin cells to form anew. We have been told by cosmetic companies to use abrasive scrubs to clean our pores from buildup (caused by over-reactivity). However, this further weakens our skin. Our skin naturally releases toxins daily, mostly during our sleep process. We can assist this process with gentle massage, but not with abrasive scrubs during a morning shower when our pores are open and ready to be cleaned. Renewal and exfoliation are a natural process in a healthy body. When I remove toxins from my skin, I use soft, natural beauty-sloughing gloves to stimulate the skin and allow its own processes to take place.

Another common skin renewal myth suggests that we need to remove layers of our skin with chemical peels or laser burning. In some ways, these practices can smooth the skin, but mostly, they are forcing a total replacement instead of a gradual one. These methods falsely assume that there are always plenty of healthy layers beneath the epidermis or the outer layer of skin. Skin renewal by stimulation is the preferred method. We do not want to weaken our skin for any reason; we should aim only to support and strengthen it. As our body's largest organ, our skin is exposed to everything in our environment all the time. It is also a protective barrier that fights against bacteria, viruses, and other external intruders trying to enter our body. It is our natural shield and should not be weakened. Our skin expands between hours of midnight until noon with peaking in the middle, from 4 a.m. until 8 a.m. The peak of expansion is when our body is ready to expel what is unused or toxic for the body. Contraction then occurs from noon until midnight, again peaking in the middle of its cycle from 4 p.m. until 8 p.m. During the peak of skin contraction is when we are most protected from the outside environment. This is part of the Circadian cycle of skin behavior.

Our body constantly monitors our skin for its current oil levels and acidic or alkaline state. This balance is important for skin maintenance and vibrancy. Creams, lotions, and makeup can have very negative effects on the pH of our skin, so become aware of which ones are most gentle on your skin. Some indications of damaged skin from high acidity include cancer, oiliness, thinness, and fatigue. When glands are abnormally acidic, our skin may become dry.

For normal, balanced, healthy skin, we must work from the inside and outside. Proper pH is important. In fact, because the pH of the blood is so important, the body has several highly effective buffer mechanisms in place to regulate it. These buffers are based on what we consume and the reactions in our system. What we eat does affect pH. Too much acid—as represented by the average diet—is manifested outwardly in fatigue of the body and mind. Aspects of the average diet that cause high acidity are processed foods, fried foods, fast foods, white breads, and improper food combinations.

When you care for your skin in a seasonal way and protect it with moisturizers made from natural botanicals, you can avoid the cracking, scaling, dry, irritated infections that many people get. Harsh treatment of our skin increases the likelihood of aggravated skin. Optimal skin does not need constant fixing; it is healthy and balanced and will naturally go through its processes.

Physical Manifestations of Toxins in the Body

When toxins are not removed from the body, they can be stored in ways that can become permanent, like cellulite, for example. The same is true of toxins created by emotional imbalance. If toxins are created in the stomach and intestinal areas, large pores may develop on the cheeks. If they are created in the colon, large pores may be seen under the chin. Hormonal imbalance creates breakouts under the chin as well. If toxins are created from the sexual organs, gall bladder, adrenal gland, liver, or kidney, the pores on both sides of the ears become enlarged. Because the toxins cannot pass through an already toxic liver, discoloration may occur in these locations.

For a man, toxicity builds up in the solar plexus area or in the pit of the stomach. He may have problems near his heart. Sometimes the chest hairs on a man turn grey and he begins to age more rapidly. When his heart is obstructed, the nose can become thick and red. Redness can also appear in his face and neck. Loss of hair in the front of the head is also another indication of toxicity. These indicators show that a man's health, attractiveness, and vitality are degenerating. Healthy strength must generate power from specific areas of the body, like muscle mass in the legs, arms, back, and thighs.

It Is Never Too Late

By the time you visibly notice unwanted signs on your face, you will realize that you have been ignoring your body's messages to you all along. Because you have recognized the problem, reassess and start again with fresh optimism and enthusiasm. Your body is very forgiving—it is never too late.

Sunscreens

Photo by Elaine Foo

Allow your body to receive the healing power of the sun!

I have never used sunscreen. Regular sunscreens block the sun, preventing our body from naturally producing Vitamin D and other nutrients. This has proven to be an unsuitable way of protecting skin from sunburns. That was a key factor in developing the formulas with the required nutrients for each season in my **Replete**™ seasonal skin care line. Choosing appropriate extracts for the minerals we need during seasonal processes ensures minimal environmental impact on our skin. In the winter, our sleep period is extended with the Winter Solstice, and we need more calicium to.improve our quality of sleep. In spring, we need zinc because it builds up the body's ability to handle the sun. As a natural sunscreen, zinc protects our skin during the spring and summer, so our cells don't break down as quickly from excessive sun exposure. Another very effective natural protector against UV-induced skin damage is an extract from Polypodium leucotomus, a fern from Central America. Conversely, bergamot, which is commonly used in Earl Grey tea, can make skin sensitive to light or more susceptible to sunburns. During the autumn, copper is important because it helps our body rebuild our summer-challenged collagen.

Years after sunscreens were created, they were discovered to contain a combination of dangerous chemicals believed to cause cancer instead of being a preventive measure against skin cancer. Not only do sunscreens block the skin´s Vitamin D production from sun exposure, but past studies also show that sunscreens caused up to 77% of all skin cancers and did not prevent burns.

Avoid sunscreens containing the following ingredients: PABA, Benzophenone, homosalate, and octy-methoxycinnamate, Parabens, Padimate-O and Parsol 1789, cinnamate, and those containing petrochemicals. Ironically, companies continue to manufacture sunscreens and cancer continues to rise. It is manipulative to incorporate sunscreen into all of our skin care products. Sunscreen is something that should be a choice when you are planning extended sun exposure and should not be forced on us through our daily cosmetics. It should not be applied on a regular basis for the very fact that it retards the body's ability to manufacture Vitamin D3, Vitamin D, and other vitamins, including micro elements still unknown to us that are directly derived from sunlight. When used continuously, sunscreen does not allow our skin to function as required for our total system management. This is when insomnia sets in, combined with weight gain, disinterest in daily activities, and lower sex drive among other problems.

By using cosmetics that do not allow your skin to breathe under any weather conditions, you are preventing your body's largest organ from breathing, absorbing, and producing vital aspects needed by our system.

According to a study done by the Italian Government, up to 40% of coral have been killed due to residuals of sunscreen lotions in our waters. Many other studies, including the "Coral Anthozoa" article in National Geographic, provide further data. The chemicals in sunscreens affect the health of algae, the food source for coral. As algae become a contaminated food source, sunscreen-induced coral bleaching occurs. Coral reefs are highly sensitive ecosystems, as are our bodies. Researchers estimate that 4,000 to 6,000 metric tons of sunscreen washes off swimmers annually in oceans worldwide. Isn't it time to consider more deeply what we have been convinced is safe to put on our skin? If necessary, use eco-friendly chemical sunscreens or sunscreens with physical filters that reflect instead of absorb ultraviolet radiation.

You can naturally boost your body's ability to tan and reduce your risk of skin cancer by eating the foods with the following nutrients: beta carotene (carrots, sweet potato, yams, pumpkin, spinach, kale, collard greens, and almost any other orange or yellow vegetable), lutein (spinach, kale, peas, Brussels sprouts, pistachios, zucchini), ECGC and polyphenols (green and black tea, cocoa, rosemary, oregano, garlic, thyme), flavonoids (citrus, especially citrus peel), cruciferous vegetables (broccoli, cauliflower, cabbage, Brussels sprouts, kale and others), fish oil, and olive oil.

Noticing Our Body and Skin's Seasonal Reactions

I have had close friends who, like me, have had allergic skin reactions to a high-end skin care product as soon as it was applied. Once, while in New York, on a very cold and brisk day, my friend and I stopped in a department store. We both tried the latest cream and then walked around the city for some hours. On the way home, I noticed my friend's eyelids had become swollen and my eyes were dreadfully red. As soon as we returned, we washed our faces and put my winter serum on our irritated skin. This immediately calmed it, and we both breathed a sigh of relief! We were surprised that my winter serum worked consistently on two very different skin types.

I know others who became violently ill, have had migraines, or suffered allergic reactions due to perfumes, odors, and chemicals in some cosmetic products. Many people have skin issues that they never associate with what they have been putting on their skin or in their bodies for years. They think that their skin problems are a chronic condition. These issues often get attributed to unknown causes. It is all very difficult to pin down, but there is a simple way of checking your reaction soon after applying a product that will most likely tell you if the choice is good. Look for a change in your energy level, check your skin's reaction, and note any signs of irritability, whether emotional or physically on your skin. Watch for delayed reactions of redness, dryness, or excessive oil production on the skin's surface. We all need to become more observant and associate symptoms with what we come in contact with or consume.

Have you ever noticed that when you try a certain skin cream, it works for a few weeks, but then, all of a sudden, you stop getting the same results? You find it causes breakouts or it makes your skin dry—it stops working. The same thing happens with shampoos, prompting people share their laments with me: "I had a shampoo and my hair was fine; my scalp was fine, and now it's flaky, dry, or oily. It just stopped working."

Through the use of skin care products, I have learned that our skin functions more effectively with seasonal care that is natural, soothing, and nourishing to our skin. It makes sense that our needs in the spring are different than our needs in the summer, autumn, and winter. The chemistry and density of our bodies change throughout the year, between dense winter solstice and expanded summer solstice and during the course of our lives. We need to adapt our skin care needs and our self-care based on our seasonal and biological clocks.

Reactions to Topicals

Photo by Deva Sexton

Some perfumes contain stimulants and allergens. Your skin sends the components of the perfume to all the sensors in our brain and in our lungs. Most perfumes are usually applied around the neck area where the thyroid is, and this should be avoided. Instead, the best places to apply perfume are on the ends of long hair or on your outer clothing. Since the thyroid is responsible for our metabolic processes, we experience stronger reactions from perfumes than other substances. Moreover, while perfumes trigger smell sensors, they also get absorbed into the blood stream.

Our thyroid gland regulates how the body uses and burns fat and then converts it to energy. It is very sensitive, delicate, and easily tired. When we force our neck and our skin to deal with stimulation from perfumes, it takes our body's attention away from normal metabolic processes. In turn, this creates sensitivity to foods, cosmetics, and airborne allergens that might not normally cause adverse reactions through physical contact or inhalation. Once our glands are fatigued, we can easily develop itches, rashes, congestions, coughs, and allergies.

The thyroid experiences overuse due to high intakes of sugar, chocolate, and caffeine. As a result, it can become over stimulated. When the thyroid becomes tired from overuse and over stimulation, you become fatigued and hungry. You may go in search of chocolate or other stimulants in order to prop your body up, creating a vicious cycle of cravings and exhaustion. This is the yo-yo effect that creates mood swings, irritability, and impatience. When the thyroid is not fully functional, it cannot support normal hormone production. In some cases, this can lead to infertility. We can also become hypersensitive to just about everything until it fails, leaving us exhausted. This weakens our immune system and may cause weight gain. Reduce the usage of stimulants like nicotine, caffeine, and other stimulating drugs to allow the thyroid gland to perform. Added protein to your diet will assist the thyroid and allow your body to flourish.

Whether we are sleep-deprived or do not get enough sunlight during the day, our body and skin cannot repair themselves, and we are left without any energy. Our hypothalamus gland loses functional balance due to exhaustion. As warning signs that our body needs help, we might experience changes in appetite, sex drive, mood, and even temperature.

Seasonal Tip:

Raspberry leaf extract is a great neutralizer and aid in dealing with an overstimulated thyroid. Sipping afternoon tea made from raspberry leaves is also very beneficial.

Primary Loss

Modern medicine has stumbled clumsily in the past with its denial of the absolute necessity for mothers to take care of their children, to touch and hold them frequently, and to breastfeed them. With the desire to promote science over nature, modern medicine and the FDA attempted to usurp a mother's ability to feed and care for her baby by substituting formula for breast milk and providing a separate room for post-natal care. The resulting *primary loss* from our earliest physical and emotional needs essential for survival. Instead of feeling safe and secure, our first experiences included a bleak sense of abandonment and abrupt feelings of loneliness. This was for the benefit of the institutions' financial gain. By derailing us from natural processes, they were able to sell more products and services. Thankfully, the social proof and the acceptance of what speaks otherwise are now finally implemented into natal care. The importance of human touch for emotional health and human development cannot be disputed.

When you stop for a moment to think rationally about where you come from—the cradling walls of the uterus, the warm amniotic sea of steady temperature and perpetual darkness—how could you possibly deny newborns the comfort of their mothers' touch across their new skin communicating their safety? Clearly, we all need to be touched and communicated with through our skin, and we need to realize its ability to communicate back to us. Healthy skin is more receptive to human touch.

The physiological intricacies of breastfeeding exemplify how perfectly we, as human beings, are designed. While a mother breastfeeds her newborn, her uterus contracts, pulling the internal and external muscle structure back into place and tightening the skin. In this way, breast-feeding naturally expedites healing and the return to a normal state for the new mother. As much as possible, it's best not to skip any part of the natural development cycle. Each part of our development represents a necessary part of our biological function and existence. Every aspect of our body and its functions have more than one purpose and are inextricably related. When we allow nature to do its work, we retain a harmony and resilience that is expressed in our vitality or ageless longevity.

My Beauty Regimen for Ageless Skin

Every morning, the first thing I do upon waking is drink a full glass of water. This begins the process of detoxification and elimination.

To optimize the use of my time without compromising personal care, the first thing I do when showering is wash my hair and put on conditioner. While the conditioner is restoring my hair, I go to work restoring my skin with shower gloves, gently massaging my body to increase circulation and remove impurities stored by my skin. I cannot stress the word "gently" enough. Gentle exfoliation helps to clear toxins from the pores and lift dead skin cells off the surface, leaving the soft skin ready to breathe. This daily massage for your skin during the shower is a wonderful time to pamper and stimulate your skin to get it ready to absorb nutrients from seasonal skin care.

This is a daily process, not a once-a-month regimen of exfoliating the top layer of skin. I use the gloves in the morning shower, because in the mornings, our body is expanded and our circulation is active. By using the shower gloves to massage my skin, I bring the gentle exfoliation to the next level of effectiveness. I keep my skin from being overstressed at all times, and I aid this organ, my skin, in processes (as explained above). After my shower, I rub my skin vigorously with a soft towel to further stimulate my skin.

When dry, I use my seasonal formulas to supplement my skin from head to toe. I do this to promote and enhance the strength of my skin against daily exposure to environmental aggravators.

At night, I take a lukewarm shower (never hot) and apply my seasonal sleep repair formula to erase the stress of daily life. The added nutrients help my body rebuild my skin during sleep. When I get out of the shower, I pat myself dry.

I also apply my healing lip balm to both my cuticles and lips to repair the soft tissues. This creates soft lips and hands without applying lip balm all day long.

This simple process is an important first step to achieving ageless skin. The gloves I use are extremely gentle and are made from natural materials, not plastic.

When I apply cosmetics, I never use foundations, and I use only the slightest amount of blush, mascara, and lipstick.

I make an effort to expose my skin to the sun at least once or twice a week. This allows my skin to develop natural sunscreen and collect enough Vitamin D for my system's necessary processes. A little daily sun acts as a healing agent and is even used for treating some skin conditions (e.g., psoriasis) and some difficult-to-heal wounds. Gradual daily sun exposure produces melanin—a process known as melanogenesis—which causes the skin to tan. Because melanin absorbs light very effectively and disperses nearly all of the absorbed UV radiation, it can help prevent sunburns. Essentially, the additional tan color acts as a sunscreen, protecting skin cells from the sun's radiation. I start my sun exposure slowly in the spring, supplementing it with my seasonal spring skin care. I do not want to end up with the intense sunburn that people get when they overexpose their skin on the first sunny day of the summer season! My seasonal spring formula is infused with zinc to help the skin adapt to more sun exposure, enabling it to resist sunburns.

Taking into consideration my experiences and the experiences of my friends and family with harmful beauty products, I have been inspired to think in terms of the way seasons support the health of our skin and bodies. Fortunately, through my curiosity and education, I have discovered natural ingredients that are wholesome choices for developing healthy skin, beautiful hair, and an essential body-care regimen. As my curiosity led me to wonder about the building blocks for healthy skin, I began to develop natural serums and creams. Using plants and botanicals that provide supportive nutrients for our bodies and skin, I asked myself which vitamins and minerals would also support our system for overall health and explored from there.

All skin products should be natural, support skin functions, and formulated with each season in mind. They should also be chemical free, time efficient, financially sound, and healthful. This is my philosophy and way of life. You, too, can apply it every day of your life through the upcoming years.

Seasonal Tip:

Use seasonal formulas for your skin relative to the hemisphere you are living in now.

Seasonal Skin Care Tips

❖ **Spring** – We begin gradually exposing our skin to daylight and warmer weather, which begins detoxifying and stimulating pigmentation for the summer.

Seasonal skin care should include zinc, Mirabelle oil, or both.

Raspberry leaf in tea or extract is good for the skin.

Turmeric is good for spring and summer skin repair. Use it on your food or as a beverage with water.

❖ **Summer**– Expose the skin to sunlight. Do not let it burn and let it breathe in the heat without any cream or oil.

Cool your skin with cooler showers all through the hot summer, especially after sun exposure. It will lower the heat impact on your overall system.

Use **Replete Intense Recovery**™ oil to assist your skin after sun exposure.

❖ **Autumn** – Our body and skin begin to tighten and close up as we start to prepare for the winter season. Your foods should be richer, with greater nutritional density.

An apple a day really does keep the doctor away. The enzymes and fiber help to stimulate the intestine to release and absorb more nutrients from your food. This also stimulates more acid production in the stomach, which prepares the body to better assimilate the nutrients your skin will need in the winter from heavier and oiled foods.

❖ **Winter** – Heavier botanical oils and extracts protect and nourish the skin, as winter foods are not rich in enzymes. This is because we grow fewer raw foods during this season.

Oils that are good to cook with in the winter months

include coconut, avocado, and pomegranate oil.

Replete Seasonal Skincare

I'm not the first to notice seasonal effects on our bodies, but I'm the first to create skincare for true seasonal function support for our skin. My skin care line is botanical-based, made from exotic plant extracts from around the world. It provides you with the nutrients to help restore your body's natural balance. This seasonal skin care will nourish and hydrate your skin during the spring, summer, autumn, and winter. These groundbreaking seasonal formulas are symbiotically tuned with our seasonal biorhythms.

For each season, we have accessed global resources for our botanically supportive extracts. We now know what we need to support our bodies in the upcoming seasons that will balance our behaviors and our moods. In our global economic environment, we can source nutrient-rich botanicals from anywhere in the world year-round. This is our Fountain of Youth, and you will have all the resources to nourish yourself with **Replete**™ seasonal formulas.

Essentially, the only thing keeping you from having ageless skin and revealing your fabulous nature are old habits, old ideas, and limited belief systems. Your youth is in your hands; you make choices every day about how you care for yourself, what you consider luxuries, and what you consider necessities. Once you recognize the symbiosis of self-care and self-healing, you will then enter an enlightened state of living.

Replete™ Seasonal Skincare Products

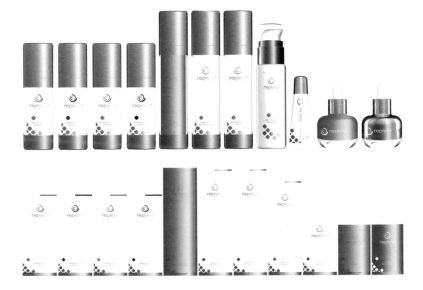

Promote beauty and balance year-round by targeting the fluctuating needs of the skin.

Why Replete™ is different:

The **Replete™** anti-aging regimen is the first of its kind to promote year-round beauty and balance based on two key biological cycles: Circadian (24 hours) and Seasonal (three months). Each product is specially formulated to enhance inherent biological processes and treats the fluctuating needs of our skin.

Ideal for every skin type, all our products are cruelty-free. Formulated with non-irritating, natural, vegan ingredients, **Replete™** Beauty products are free of chemicals, fragrances, artificial dyes, silicones, parabens, and glycol.

Deep Clean Restore™

This nourishing daily cleanser gently sweeps away impurities, makeup, and excess oil while maintaining skin's natural moisture barrier. Its natural bioactive ingredients gently exfoliate to promote a smoother, more radiant-looking complexion. **Deep Clean Restore™** detoxifies and purifies skin, enhances cell renewal, and improves capillary circulation and firmness.

- ❖ Rinses easily and leaves skin feeling soft and pristinely clean.
- ❖ Prepares your skin for the absorption of serums and creams.

Spring Serum Complex™

Specially formulated for springtime use, this antioxidant-rich, anti-inflammatory treatment enhances cell renewal and resilience, while protecting skin from seasonal environmental stressors and allergens. A proprietary, globally sourced blend, Seasonal Actives™ help improve skin's tone, texture, and overall health.

- ❖ Promotes refreshed, radiant, healthy skin.

- ❖ Restores vibrancy and reduces skin matrix degradation.

- ❖ Its continual hydration plumps and revitalizes your skin.

- ❖ Helps visibly correct the signs of photo-aging (sun damage) and protects against further damage.

- ❖ Advanced stabilizing enzymes boost collagen and elastin while preventing fine lines and sagging.

- ❖ Prevents DNA degradation to ensure healthy cell reproduction.

Summer Serum Complex™

Specially formulated for summertime use, this antioxidant-rich, anti-stress treatment enhances cellular rejuvenation and oxygenation while protecting the skin and its DNA from seasonal environmental stressors (e.g., extreme climate). Proprietary, globally-sourced Seasonal Actives™ help improve skin's tone, texture, and overall health.

❖ Supports skin's natural Vitamin D production and defends against UVA and UVB damage.

❖ Visibly corrects signs of photo-aging and helps prevent further damage.

❖ Helps reduce the appearance of fine lines and wrinkles.

❖ Gently removes dead skin cells with natural exfoliators.

❖ Boosts collagen and elastin production.

❖ Promotes skin oxygenation and detoxification.

❖ Restores skin's vibrancy and reduces skin matrix degradation.

❖ Continually hydrates to plump and revitalize skin.

Autumn Serum Complex™

Specially formulated for autumn use, this intensely nourishing treatment helps repair summer-induced damage and visibly corrects signs of photo-aging. Proprietary, globally-sourced Seasonal Actives™ help improve skin's tone, texture, and overall health in preparation for the dry, cold months ahead.

❖ Builds a resistance barrier to ward off the elements.

❖ Boosts hydration and radiance by stimulating natural hyaluronic acid production and lipidic homeostasis.

❖ Comforts, smoothens, and redensifies thin and fragile skin.

❖ Restores skin vibrancy and reduces skin matrix degradation.

❖ Helps prevent and reduce the appearance of premature lines, wrinkles, and sagging.

Winter Serum Complex™

Specially formulated for winter use, this hydrating treatment provides 24-hour comfort and protection from seasonal environmental stressors like extreme cold and artificial indoor heat. Proprietary Seasonal Actives™ sourced from Antarctica help prevent premature aging by improving the skin's hydration capacity and overall well-being.

❖ Promotes optimal moisture retention within skin cells.

❖ Boosts radiance and cell resilience through increased collagen synthesis.

❖ Helps prevent and reduce the appearance of premature lines, wrinkles, and sagging.

❖ Enhances cellular rejuvenation and restores skin's vibrancy.

❖ Strengthens the outer layer of the skin.

Circadian 365 Day Cream™

Specially formulated to enhance the skin's inherent biological process or "circadian rhythm," this anti-aging, anti-inflammatory cream promotes optimal health and cell renewal. Proprietary, globally sourced Circadian Actives™ purify, protect, and soothe skin from daily environmental stressors. **Circadian 365 Day Cream™** should be applied after the Seasonal Serum™.

- ❖ Improves the vitality of all skin layers.

- ❖ Instantly reduces the appearance of fine lines and improves the texture and smoothness of skin within four weeks.

- ❖ Extends cell longevity and maintains skin's firmness.

- ❖ Protects against elastin degradation.

- ❖ Boosts hydration by stimulating natural hyaluronic acid production.

- ❖ Evens skin tone and texture for a brighter, more luminous complexion.

Rejuvenating Mist™

Rehydrate your skin and replenish lost nutrients with our deep ocean water mist. This **Rejuvenating Mist™** prevents wrinkle formation from free radicals and helps the skin deal with fluctuating climates, hormones, stress, and circadian cycles.

- ❖ Rapidly neutralizes stressful changes in humidity and salts to help keep skin balanced.

- ❖ Promotes optimal moisture retention within skin cells.

- ❖ Strengthens your skin's natural barrier.

- ❖ Simultaneously soothes and energizes exhausted skin by boosting and improving your skin's defenses.

- ❖ Creates that *fresh out of the shower* look any time of the day.

Spray your skin lavishly with the **Rejuvenating Mist™** after cleansing and as desired throughout the day, or use it to set your makeup for a radiant finish.

Lip Restore™

Our moisture-intense, high-performing balm restores fullness and softness by hydrating, protecting, and healing dry, cracked lips.

❖ Restores fullness and moisture to depleted lips.

❖ Protects from impacts of climates.

❖ Smoothens and softens the contours of the lips.

Lip Restore™ can be applied to lips for instant comfort and protection. Ideal for use while traveling by airplane, yachting, biking, or changing time zones. Great for moisturizing cuticles or fast healing of minor paper cuts.

Eye Restore™

Our unique antioxidant-rich, antibacterial, and anti-inflammatory treatment helps maintain bright and youthful-looking eyes and lids, imparting a well-rested glow. Helps diminish lines, puffiness and dark circles and promotes better beauty sleep for total circadian recovery. Sesame oil and powerful carotenes protect the skin from premature aging and wrinkles.

❖ Helps restore the appearance of youthful eyes.

❖ Helps diminish fine lines, wrinkles, dark circles, and puffiness.

❖ Relieves fatigue and tension in the surrounding eye area.

❖ Penetrates the skin easily.

Use **Eye Restore™** after washing your face in the evening; sweep a pre-soaked cotton ball or pad in an outward-facing direction over the eyelid and under the eye. **Eye Restore™** also easily removes stubborn eye makeup.

Circadian 365 Night Cream™

Specially formulated to enhance the skin's inherent biological process or "circadian rhythm," this advanced anti-aging cream promotes nightly cell repair and detoxification. Proprietary, globally sourced Circadian Actives™ promote a radiant, rested-looking complexion by morning. **Circadian 365 Night Cream™** should be applied after the Seasonal Serum.

❖ Helps restore elasticity, luminosity, and radiance.

❖ Instantly reduces the appearance of fine lines while improving the texture and smoothness of skin within four weeks.

- ❖ Boosts collagen production for firm, supple skin.

- ❖ Repairs oxidative DNA damage and protects from cellular degradation.

- ❖ Increases cellular respiration and ATP energy levels.

- ❖ Purifies and detoxifies to promote cell longevity.

- ❖ Evens skin tone and texture for a brighter, healthier, younger-looking complexion.

Intense Recovery Oil™

A deeply healing formula with world wide-sourced ingredients that help restore and rebuild skin recovering from extensive travel, sun exposure, photo facials or other modern cosmetic procedures. Helps speed skin's recovery after undergoing skin resurfacing procedures such as peels and laser resurfacing.

- ❖ Calms, comforts, and rebuilds stressed, sensitive skin.

- ❖ Helps restore skin to a smoother, suppler, more youthful appearance.

Apply a thin layer morning and night after washing, or as needed.

Replete Aqua™

Replete Aqua™ is your source for total mineral replenishment, providing you with an abundance of energy for everything you like to do. This naturally pristine water is drawn from a depth of 3,000 feet off the Hawaiian coast. At this depth, the naturally pure 2,000-year-old water is completely unaffected by today's pollutants, and contains more than 20 times the mineral content of the surface layer.

❖ The ionic minerals are easily absorbed by the body.

❖ High in magnesium, calcium, potassium, and 90 other trace minerals for healthy bones, teeth, blood, heart, and digestion; increased fat burn; and improved nerve transmission.

❖ Recovers and restores digestive and assimilative functions of the intestinal tract.

Drink 2-4 ounces daily, preferably in the evening.

Please visit ***www.repleteskincare.com*** to see our complete product line.

Photo by Joshua Horowitz

CHAPTER THREE

OUR SIX SENSES

Heart, Sight, Hearing, Smell, Touch, and Taste

An individual's personality traits can be divided into the following categories based on our six senses: heart, sight, hearing, smell, touch, and taste. These senses translate to sensory traits and coincide with one's daily habits that may include food preferences, desires, interpersonal relationships, career results, physical regimen, hours needed for sleep, and emotional trigger points. A person's sensory trait is greatly determined by their sensory dominance (i.e., the sense that dominates or influences their personality the most).

Heart Sense

With a strong heart sense, these people tend to be the most balanced between all senses and can draw on all qualities based on their current demand. Heart sense people process on a multi-dimensional level, crossing over all the senses.

The heart assesses intention faster than any other sense. We often refer to it as a *gut feeling* because we feel something intuitively or instinctually.

Sight Sense

This personality type is childlike, so those with a strong sense of sight tend to be perceived as dreamers, often taking careers in philosophy, science, and development where they can focus within their own world at their own pace. These people find comfort and pleasure in film and painting.

Our mind can only process light at 40 frames per second; any faster and we become overloaded.

Hearing Sense

People with this creative personality can have tremendous bursts of energy and artistry. They are best suited for creative professions involving art, music, or writing. "Sound-centric" people like symphonies and music. They are the most linear and are happiest with earphones on experiencing a constant stream of sound.

Smell Sense

With a tracker's personality, people aligned with a strong sense of smell are always on the hunt for something new and exciting. As pursuers, they love being the center of attention and in control of their environment. Thus, preferring to direct, they take charge by always employing others to do the hard work. Choreography is for people who respond to body movement like dancing—even absent of sound.

Touch Sense

People connected to the sense of touch have even-tempered personalities and like to operate in harmonious environments. They love spending time with family and friends and do not like to be alone. These nurturers love peacc and tend to stay away from competition. People with touch sense personalities appreciate 3D, sculpture, and ballet.

Taste Sense

People with personalities linked to the sense of taste exhibit great stamina with more awake hours and are likely to have athletic physiques. Having the most resilient of all personality types, taste sense people generally have a strong presence and are attracted to the culinary arts.

A choice of art and physical activity is also determined by your dominant sense.

Our Senses and Their Corresponding Body/Exercise/Art References

Heart—Heart—Sleep, Walking—Balance of all Arts

Sight—Pituitary—Martial Arts—Paintings

Hearing—Thyroid—Weight Training—Reading

Smell—Reptilian Brain—Talking—Music

Touch—Sex glands—Yoga, Pilates—Sculptures

Taste—Adrenal—Swimming—Ballet

Hierarchic Relationship between Two Principles

Creative	in contrast to	Receptive
Nature	in contrast to	Spirit
Earth	in contrast to	Heaven
Space	in contrast to	Time
Female Maternal	in contrast to	Male Paternal

This duality appears in the coexistence of the spiritual world and the world of senses we live, in calling on physical proof for existence, recognition, or acceptance.

Support from the Heart

Acting from a coherent heart is essential to our balance in life. The heart forms an energy circuit that regulates brain function through a heart and brain interface.

- ❖ Sensory information (vibrational patterns) comes to the heart from our environment. These patterns alter heart rate variations depending on whether they are coherent or incoherent. For example, when a person enters a room, your reaction can be one of great joy (i.e., coherent presence) or one of great discomfort (i.e., incoherent presence).

❖ There are more nerve fibers going from the heart to the brain than the other way around. The heart stimulates the medulla oblongata (i.e., having to do with action and our survival reflexes), the thalamus (i.e., having to do with incoming sensory information) and the amygdala of the limbic system (i.e., having to do with emotions and memory, and therefore, formulating our perceptions).

❖ If the heart frequencies are coherent (as with joy, appreciation, humor), the amygdala directs the parasympathetic nervous system to function (e.g., normal heart rate, blood pressure, breathing) and increases the baroreceptors to the thalamus, so it easily takes in sensory information (i.e., learning). The amygdala also directs a coherent brain wave pattern in the pre-frontal cortex, which allows the brain to easily receive incoming information, synthesize it, and create new ideas with it. This truly calls for creating a relaxed and loving environment.

❖ If the heart frequencies are incoherent as with stress and survival, the amygdala directs the sympathetic nervous system to activate adrenalin and cortisol, decreasing baroreceptors to the thalamus. So, the thalamus only takes in sensory information that is directly related to survival. It lowers our magnetic frequencies during that process. The amygdala also directs an incoherent brain wave pattern in the pre-frontal cortex, which then prevents all incoming information from making sense or being placed in the memory. Predatory and manipulative people often apply this technique of using fear to create incoherence in order to render their prey defenseless. Experiencing chronic incoherence sets up brain wave patterns that result in a comfortable, homeostatic state for the person. These people, if put into a coherent situation, will *stir things up* just to create incoherence and make themselves feel more at home. It often can be a post-traumatic symptom from a previous scenario. We often witness this in children labeled as hyperactive, or having Attention Deficit Disorder (ADD), or being emotionally handicapped.

❖ The coherent heart/brain wave pattern is the most natural for our system. When we feel stress, frustration, or anger, if we just stand up and bring our attention to the heart, the heart will naturally settle back into coherence.

❖ The heart's energy amplitude is 60 times greater than that of the brain, and the energy field from it extends between three and eight feet. Sometimes, it expands as much as 12 feet, resembling a torus around the body when measured by a SQUID (i.e., an instrument that discovers and measures faint magnetic fields). Thus, when we bring ourselves into coherence and stand within six feet of another person with an incoherent pattern, that person's heart rate and brain waves will entrain ours. In other words, that person's incoherence will be pulled or modified by our rhythms until it eventually reaches coherence. This is known as *having a calming effect.*

❖ Rhythmic breathing, focusing on the heart, knowing that all of the pieces of the balancing process are perfect in their ability to bring coherence will enable us to set up a safe heart. This will be the place that we can make the life changes we choose.

The heart has been the center of traditional Chinese Medicine and Yogi for thousands of years. According to Western culture, the neocortex of the brain is the first and only measure of reality. As a result of disconnecting from nature, we are experiencing a major crisis in education, health, and social indifference. Then, how does one acquire a coherent state of the heart?

* One has to have ultimate faith in her own ability to learn and change.

* The person helping must have absolute faith in her own healing ability.

* The one undertaking it has to have the sense of curiosity and wonder to go through the process of transition into living with a coherent heart.

In each case, the person exposed to the process is consciously seeing the other as a complex being and is directly connected to them in the journey for wisdom and learning. We might miss the boat by fine-tuning our techniques and levels of perfection with a practitioner who may not be the right person to aid our progress. Before our heart energy is straightened out, we have to use our own judgment to determine if we have found the right person to help us.

There are three KEY ELEMENTS for Optimal Balancing:

❖ INTENTIONALITY—Heart-driven.

❖ BEING ATTENTIVE—Totally conscious, focused, and honestly sincere in every action.

❖ ENTHUSIASTIC, CURIOUS, AND READY FOR DISCOVERY AND JOY—Seeing with beginner's eyes as an adventure in and of itself.

Importance of Touch

Jungle dogs reaching out for human touch.

Photo by Eduardo de la Cerda

Our skin is a conduit for our emotional well-being. Massage boosts the immune system by increasing the number and lethal power of natural "killer cells," white blood cells that, among other functions, help suppress burgeoning tumors. According to Elizabeth Scott, M.S., 90 percent of health issues are stress-related. Given that massage was one of the earliest forms of medicine, this underscores that human touch significantly benefits our health. Stimulating and massaging the skin the right way releases growth factors and hormones that act positively on the central nervous system. Essentially, massage allows the body to heal itself. So, if we can reduce anxiety and stress through bodywork, the resulting positive feelings will help alleviate fatigue, counter the signs of aging, and improve our concentration and energy.

Overstimulation Affects Us

What we may not know is that our body is working overtime, processing the sensory stimulation of wind hitting our skin. We must be mindful of the environmental elements we are exposing our skin to, not only because of the obvious effect on our skin, but also because of the effects on our moods, energy, and behaviors. This explains why so many people get cranky and irritable on windy days!

Clothing can also be an unpleasant stimulus for our skin. Wearing comfortable clothing in layers is very important for regulating body temperature and wellness. For children who may not have the best communication skills, Rudolf Steiner repeatedly stresses the importance of keeping them dressed in comfortable, safe, easy-to-remove layers of clothing to avoid becoming too hot or too cold. This allows them to focus on their life experiences without pain, discomfort, and distraction.

What constitutes overstimulation varies from person to person and is based on the sensory group in which one belongs. Overstimulation can cause negative moods and stresses, making the source or agent practically unidentifiable.

Even if we are unable to identify the causes, we can still take a closer look at the changes in our senses themselves that lead to our moods' shifts. By paying attention to which senses start declining when environmental stressors become too overwhelming, we can get better insight about our own sensory personality. In doing so, this helps us learn ways to circumvent these discomforts and better understand how to maintain a more balanced lifestyle. Essentially, each sensory personality group experiences the effects of overstimulation differently with correlating sense failures. In other words, when particular sensors are overstimulated, they become desensitized or degraded in their inherent functions:

❖ Skin lacks receptiveness to touch.

❖ Taste loses ability to detect flavors.

❖ Hearing declines, leaving amplitudes of sounds indiscernible.

❖ Sight fails to decipher the meaning of actions.

❖ Smell misses nuances of scents.

❖ Feeling no longer distinguishes the value of intentions.

Thus, the senses that normally define our personality by being the most pronounced and optimal will be suddenly rendered inoperative and inadequate with excessive stimuli.

On the other hand, the absence of stimuli can be so maddening that it has been used as a form of severe punishment. In fact, the lack of human interaction—the absence of stimulus—serves as punishment in a silent asylum (i.e., solitary confinement) and paradoxically becomes the stimulus or the very agent of the punishment itself.

Stimulating Food Types:

❖ Creamy foods stimulate our social skills and patience.

❖ Fat-free dairy and fruits deliver stamina and accuracy.

- ❖ Spicy foods stimulate sex drive.

- ❖ Greasy meats and alcohol stimulate aggressive posture and drive for physical tasks.

- ❖ Caffeine and sugar enhance creativity.

Sensory Balancers

Helpful ways of restoring balance to each sensory system:

- ❖ **Heart Sense**–Get extra sleep and occasionally have honey before bed.

- ❖ **Sight Sense**–Sarsaparilla, ginseng, and fenugreek.

- ❖ **Hearing Sense**–Kelp in any form and raspberry leaf extract.

    - ❖ No use of caffeine is best.

- ❖ **Smell Sense**–Drink cool water throughout the day.

- ❖ **Touch Sense**–Dong Quai and Cohosh.

- ❖ **Taste Sense**–Licorice root, Buchu leaf, parsley tea or black tea. We should pay closer attention to our daily biological energy clock. We can then supply what is needed for strength to finish the day successfully.

Dr. Tanzeem Choudhury of Cornell University is developing a smartphone app called *StressSense*. By using the microphones embedded in smartphones, *StressSense* inconspicuously monitors and analyzes changes in speech (i.e., changes in amplitudes and frequencies of sound) that occur with stress. Because *StressSense* can detect voice-based stress, it can help reveal the causes of stress. Dr. Choudhury also has an app available now called *BeWell* that focuses on overall health and tracks sleep patterns, physical activity, and social interaction. This app serves as a tool to help analyze the onset of depression, as well as other health problems.

We can easily support our energy pitfalls by eating or avoiding certain foods during very specific times of the day and night. We are ultimately in control of how we feel and the level at which we perform daily. So why does this matter? Proper nourishment boosts energy and alleviates fatigue. If you give your body the balance it needs for optimal performance, you will actualize your ideal weight, energy, and a positive, logical mind.

We only gain or lose weight when our system is stressed or overburdened.

For example, if you are a **sound** driven person and are inclined to live on stimulants, caffeine, sweets, and chocolates, then you are probably prone to be tired by 4 p.m. You should have protein in the morning, preferably eggs, while avoiding carbohydrates and caffeine. This will provide steady energy throughout the day.

Conversely, if you are a **taste** driven person, you are likely living on steaks, potatoes, ice cream, and hard cheese, and you will be tired by 5 p.m. In this case, a caffeinated beverage will boost your energy.

This is the time to recognize our individuality and follow a unique, self-created regimen that works for you.

The adage that breakfast is the most important meal of the day is a myth. We should tailor how and what we eat according to our sensory personality traits.

If you feed breakfast to a **touch** sensory person, it would lead to obesity super fast by imparting a frustrated, tired state of mind and body. Instead, the best meal of the day is dinner. Panax, ginger, and even a little caffeine are helpful to balance the body. Staying away from soft cheeses will help a touch sensory person feel energized and stay slim from the waist down.

A **visually** driven person needs to start the day with salty and protein-rich foods to get them through the day easily and productively. This is the main meal of the day.

People who are driven by a sense of **smell**, with their reptilian

118

brains, do best with vegetarian meals and plenty of water to balance their naturally strong and intense system. They thrive on small meals throughout the day.

Last, but not least, **heart** driven people that process all five other senses are the most interesting when it comes to balancing. They can actually switch between all five sensory systems as needed. They design their stamina based on their current needs.

If one of your systems are off, you would do best to rely on your sixth sense, your **heart**. **Logic** only applies when all the other senses have participated in assessing the situation.

See how different we all are. There is beauty in our diversity.

My Be Fabulous At Any Age Notes:

Importance of Music and Other Arts

Photo by Timothy Williamson

The arts were created to stimulate our senses. They stimulate flow and experience. Ultimately, our bodies do not like stagnation.

Music can evoke memories, emotions, and tremendous enjoyment. Some types of classical music have been shown to improve IQs, particularly the works of Beethoven and Mozart. Known as *the Mozart Effect*, the frequencies in classical music place the mind in highly distinctive states that increase neurotransmitters and can improve spatial-temporal reasoning. Early exposure to classical music can have beneficial effects on mental development from birth on. Conversely, listening to punk, metal, and rock music can have a degenerative effect on your brain, as this type of music is generally chaotic in nature, and the frequencies are not in harmony with each other.

Learning to play a musical instrument has been shown to increase the capacity to concentrate. People who play instruments tend to be smarter in many ways and are more likely to excel in mathematics. When we use any part of our bodies, it is strengthened. Thus, by engaging your mind in learning to play music or through listening to music, your brain will function better.

Music and mathematics are universal languages.

Mothers who expose their unborn children to classical music tend to have easier deliveries and healthier babies.

Now, the medical field is turning to music as an alternative to anesthesia, which leaves patients with severe brain function side effects. Instead of resorting to drugs, Dr. Stankovic has been working with anesthesiologists to develop heart-calming effects prior to surgery with a pulse-music feedback system. Harmonics and symmetry have the same impact through different senses. Other specialists have been implementing surgery through lasers without cutting the skin, targeting only the problematic areas.

Seasonal Tip:

Enjoy music as an indoor or evening activity when you are alone or entertaining. Music brightens the soul.

Photo by Liza Gershman

CHAPTER FOUR

OUR PHYSICAL HEALTH

We Only Have One Body

Our physical health is vitally important for a desirable, good life. If you ever doubt that, look at the quality of life of a physically impaired animal, and maybe then you will be willing to assign your time to care for your body without thinking it frivolous or unnecessary. This is what nature teaches us. In our lifetime, we are given only one body. When our body fails, we become dependent on others for our survival or for their kindness, generosity, and good intentions. Without it, we die slowly from hunger and decay, just like impaired animals in the wild.

Our level of motivation for activities is seasonal and nutrient-related. It is important that we maintain movement both inside—through organ-stimulating yoga poses and stretching—and outside for muscle strength and joint alignment.

Our interest in and need for activities are related to many factors, including the month in which we were born. The foods that work best for us will determine our body's needs and energy levels.

They are all tied together. For instance, in addition to a woman's emotional state, the food that she eats during her pregnancy will affect her child's constitution, their mental, physical, and spiritual health, and the ability to adapt socially.

Experience No Fatigue

When you are in optimal health, you should not feel abnormally tired. Fatigue should not be an ongoing condition. If we constantly desire change—changing our minds, ideas, plans, or addresses—or if we are too rigid and unwilling to progress and advance through change, we are not in a healthy state. Neither extreme is healthy. Health is a state of harmonizing with our environment and using our resources to do so. Proper exercises aid in getting the sleep we need for demanding days, helping us control and deal with temptations along the way. Thus, proper amounts of sleep and exercises promote healthy appetites to acquire our body's nutritional needs. Life without the added stimulation of our endorphins during the day, and without sleep aids that chemically force our systems to sleep during the night, will prevent premature aging on both a physical and mental level. It will keep us playful!

Six Sense Needs for Different Nutrients

Conventional approaches to nutrition do not speak to the ever-changing states of our bodies and our environments. Where each person needs a specific balance of carbohydrates, vitamins, minerals, proteins, and fats each day, the conventional approach does not take into consideration our uniqueness or our changing needs. This eventually leads to stagnant thinking. My approach to daily living requires the transition from static thinking to one that is dynamic and flexible.

Your basic nature is a given, although you may acquire or wish to access other characteristics of another sense. You can do this by consuming the appropriate foods, exercising, and learning. For example, if you need creative energy to awaken your **smell** sense, then give yourself thyroid-stimulating foods. Exercise creates a heightened sense of taste and helps you feel strong. When you need brainpower to stay on task, treat yourself to dairy products and your heightened **sight** sense will ignite.

In a similar way, you can get ready for a party and enhance your social skills by consuming fat-rich foods for help just before the guests arrive. Your **touch** sensory traits will emerge, and you may be described as touchy-feely during the party. This again proves how everything is connected. Our metabolism influences how we think, what we like to eat, and how food transforms us once it enters our body.

Give Your Body a Break Every Week

Give your digestive system a day off every week. Try to choose the slowest day of the week to minimize your food intake, and then rest from noon until noon the next day. This is the easiest way to cover all bodily functions and give the organs a break. By giving the digestive organs the opportunity to repair themselves without the interruption of digesting new foods, your digestive system will then serve you better by bouncing back stronger.

Our Breath Is Movement

Our breath is what we take most for granted, and yet we cannot live without it. We often discount the obvious: we enter this world by taking our first breath, and we leave it when we cannot breathe anymore. With conscious breathing, we can control the speed of our heart, raise or lower our body temperature, and control our anxiety and pain. In fact, with conscious breathing, women give birth to children! Through our breath, we are able to quiet ourselves into the present moment.

Breathing air is more than just a physiological act of survival. Considered the basis of life, breath is known as prana[1], which makes us mentally secure, physically stronger, and increases our immunity against illness.

Practicing good breathing patterns provides clear thinking and will give you the ability to make better decisions. Moreover, it will keep your overall system better oxygenated to run smoother.

Our breath affects all of our internal organs just like waves on the edge of the sea. It moves fluids in our organs and between them the same way the waves move on the bottom of the ocean, constantly bringing new water and caressing the surface of the sand. Only 80 percent of our breath that enters through the nose goes to our lungs. From the nose, our system distributes air components

---

[1] The Sanskrit word for "life"

to the digestive and circulatory systems, in addition to the lungs for detoxification. Twenty percent of inhaled air is purified in the sinuses to be utilized by our brain.

Breathing well does not come as naturally as we would assume. The poor postures we have acquired after long days of sitting at desks do not allow us to breathe deeply. We actually need to become aware of the positions we assume, so our breath reaches into us with greatest ease and effect. Inhale deeply and notice where the air goes and how it feels.

Starting with the breath as our primary exercise that delivers internal movement for our organs, we can now change our relationship with our body and mind. Take this opportune moment to assess the source of any discomfort that is emotional or physical in nature. The next step of this breathing exercise is to channel awareness of the source of that discomfort. This will lead to the solution and the eventual elimination of the symptoms and their sources. Even if they are only a part of our imagination, this does not make them any less valid. They all can lead to chronic illness.

For example, certain asthmatic breathing conditions are aggravated at various times in an asthmatic's life and can be triggered by food additives, dairy, and other allergens. Quite often, asthma is induced by strong emotions (i.e., those that cause fear or anger). If we pay close attention to how the body and mind respond to exposures to food, situations, and people, we can better evaluate what is good or bad for us. Ultimately, this helps balance the connection with our body and mind. Our daily or weekly breathing sessions will also most likely bring the right answers to us.

Dr. Swetak Patel gathers information from our breath through an iPhone app called *SpiroSmart*. The software app analyzes the resonance from the breath expelled through the trachea and past the vocal cords. By estimating lung air volume, the *SpiroSmart* app helps diagnose and control COPD, cystic fibrosis, and chronic asthma.

Here's a quick way to become calm through a simple breathing exercise:

- ❖ Count to two and inhale; then, count to two again and exhale

- ❖ Repeat until your breathing evens out and becomes comfortable.

- ❖ Increase to a count of three while you inhale, and three while you exhale (approximately 10 breaths).

- ❖ Increase to a count of four gradually, and after about 10 more breaths, you will be in what is referred to as a therapeutic state.

You will have downshifted your nervous system!

As you slow your breath, you may experience some changes: gurgling in your stomach (organs draining and releasing), a softening of your vision, or you might yawn and feel sleepy. These are positive changes; just stick with it, and any discomfort will pass. Just five minutes of slow breathing a day can improve your body's healing ability and enhance your health.

Seasonal Tip:

The quietest time of the breath is just between inhaling and exhaling. When you do it with a sigh, you are on your way to finding balance.

Neuromuscular Reset

Neuromuscular reset (NMR) is the most effective way to hold and restore our body in its original, aligned healthy state. According to Jocelyn Olivier, CMT, MBW:

> *The focus of NMR is to create better integrated and coordinated bodies; consciously illuminating the kinesthetic blind spots of sensory motor amnesia is a huge step in our conscious evolution toward highly integrated functioning. The*

unexpected benefits of reducing the energy demand from the support and movement system by improving neuromuscular efficiency are more energy, clearer vision, increase in muscle definition through normalization of tissue metabolism, and more energy available for the higher brain functions of creative thought and problem solving.

Psychologically, it means a greater sense of well-being, feeling balanced and whole. As clients report a return to energy levels remembered from a much younger age, we realize that the more we can reduce stress on the system created by the dysfunctional neuromuscular connections, the easier their lives become.

Seasonal Activities and Exercise

It is important to find and develop seasonal activities for the benefit of your mental, spiritual, and physical health. Seasonal hobbies and interests underscore the concept of seasonal change and transitions. They also lay the foundation for traditional and social behaviors that connect us with our environment.

Exercise is usually dependent on the season as well. If it is snowing, most people are not going to go out and run three miles.

Cloaked in tradition, our activities are linked to the seasons. All professional sports have a season, as do schools, teams, and groups. Exercise is a seasonal activity for vacations. Outdoor enjoyment and travel tie together as they become part of the fabric of our lives and the lives of our children. It is what we use to build memories, traditions, and a sense of belonging within groups, families, and communities.

In the spring/summer, we may garden, hike, ride bikes, or vacation. In the autumn/winter, we gather together for indoor activities, cooking, and cold-weather sports. There are many forms of exercise available to you for your emotional and physical satisfaction. Our body needs movement and resistance to increase strength, but it is our mental satisfaction that brings us back to doing it again. There is no hard-and-fast rule about the type of exercise or how much of it we need, except that we must pay attention to, and listen to our bodies, adjusting accordingly. Choose the form of exercise that you enjoy and relate to, and that will ensure the success of your continued regimen.

Your early activity sets the foundation for your future activity and that of your family's. Rooting your exercise regimen into seasonal tradition further enables your family to follow seasonal living with ease.

CHAPTER FOUR - OUR PHYSICAL HEALTH

We can change our bodies and the quality of our life through diet, exercise, and seasonal lifestyle. When we partake in the best of what the seasons have to offer, we can benefit from what was designed for us naturally. As an athlete, I found my body wouldn't cooperate if I extended my seasonal sport from one season to another. However, my body was more than willing and eager to engage in sports vigorously in the appropriate season. Life has its natural rhythm of recurring changes.

Seasonal Feel-Fabulous Choices

- ❖ **Spring** – Treat yourself to something you do not do all the time. Get out and do a body scrub. Cleanse to detoxify and remove your winter skin layers.

- ❖ **Summer** – Rinse with lukewarm water that complements your summer skin after sun exposure. (Avoid hot water for summer showers.)

- ❖ **Autumn** – Begin the autumn with a wrap of botanicals with seaweed, dead-sea mud, or lavender.

- ❖ **Winter** – A wrap of basil poultice elevates mood and offsets lack of sunlight. Do this twice in the winter.

Photo by Elaine Foo

CHAPTER FIVE

EXERCISE

Walking

I walk daily to provide circulation to my body and spine.

Walking is good for just about anyone, and the health benefits are particularly significant for women. Here are some good reasons to start walking:

- ❖ Promotes healthy heart.

- ❖ Reduces the risk of heart disease, diabetes, and stroke.

- ❖ Reduces the risk of breast cancer.

- ❖ Reduces levels of body fat.

- ❖ Aids in sleep.

- ❖ Boosts levels of serotonin for relaxation.

- ❖ Aids digestion, so it reduces colon cancer risk.

- ❖ Reduces aches and pains.

- ❖ Lubricates the joints.

- ❖ Our spine receives needed circulation for the nourishment of the nerves.

Walking provides the necessary circulation to the spine and nourishes our nerves because our spine does not have independent circulation. Exercising our bodies reduces the risk of many illnesses, including heart disease, diabetes, and other cancers. If you have already been diagnosed with cancer, exercise can still help. Most people do not realize how important it is to develop strong muscles in our legs. It is the muscle in our legs that aids the heart in circulating the blood and lymphatic fluids throughout our system.

Strong legs = Strong heart.

Just a 30-minute walk has been shown to do the trick. You will reduce your risk of a number of health issues. Along with the physical benefits, the emotional and mental benefits help you feel better so you're able to function better. It also helps with thermal stability, enabling you to regulate your body temperature.

While I stress the importance of body movement, and the fact that you can find a variety of activities to participate in, I must also be clear that it is rhythm and routine, guided by seasonal awareness, which will simplify and de-stress your life.

CHAPTER FIVE - EXERCISE

Yoga

Yoga is an exercise designed for internal organs. Because of its profound whole-body results in assisting the support of our physiological and psychological well-being, yoga can be used to counteract many physical problems, addictions, and postural difficulties. Yoga is a life-extending practice.

You benefit by releasing trapped energy in stored fat or tension through deep breathing, allowing the body to harmonize and cleanse. This is the internal system at work. In aerobic exercise, the blood is pumped more forcefully through the heart, but the work of the lymph is done through muscle contraction and respiratory diaphragm movement. When we are engaged in deep breathing, exercising, and sweating, we facilitate the body's ability to cleanse itself of toxins and waste. Some names and practices of yoga include Hatha Yoga (great for beginners since all the yoga poses are done gently) and Pranayama (studying the breath), which comes from "prana," the Sanskrit word for life force or vital energy. It is our vital energy that creates and sustains our ageless longevity, beautiful skin, and attitudes.

Yoga postures help realign the body by stretching and relaxing the muscles so that problems can be stopped before they start. Yoga uncovers underlying causes for stress, pain, and tension, and leads to more permanent and healthy resolutions.

Other Types of Exercise

❖ **Weight Lifting**: Adds bone density and strength.

❖ **Martial Arts**: Heightens our awareness, increases agility and strength with flexibility.

❖ **Swimming**: Best form of physical therapy and rehabiliation, as the body's buoyancy in water allows people to execute movements easily, offering the best range of motion for the joints.

❖ **Golf**: Mental exercise for focus between body and mind.

Photo by Joshua Horowitz

Golfing at Turnberry in Scotland, where golf originated.

Photo by Liza Gershman

142

CHAPTER SIX

OUR EMOTIONAL HEALTH

We have come to reconcile that energy of emotion and matter are one and the same.

The order of development in our emotional consciousness follows us throughout our lives. Consciousness is being aware of ourselves, our surroundings, how we are affected through our senses, and how we affect others. It is a matter of being present.

The circumstance of inability to function as a complete adult is the result of an incomplete transition during puberty. Conscious ego is one that transitions from unconscious to conscious during puberty. It is fragile ground, but more easily adapted to and resolved if the foundation of living within the framework of cycles, seasons, and routine has been established early on. If not, the conscious ego begins to repress the unconscious ego, resulting in an overvaluation of oneself. This is a sign of immature consciousness and may be compensated with extreme emotions, such as self-destructive hatred or even suicide as one of the symptoms in puberty. The other face of hatred is directing negative thoughts at family members or animals. Narcissism is a transitional phase of the ego during the consolidation period and is dangerous when one becomes stuck in one's developmental stage of puberty by not completing this important cycle.

By going through pre-planned experiences of purposeful change in our environment on a seasonal basis (every three months), we become more adaptable to unexpected change, which makes us more successful in overcoming adversity.

After the states of adolescence and narcissism are resolved, then we move into the next phase of development, which is empathy. Only after that is completed do we become grounded adults who have a deep understanding of self-feeling and experience as a reference point. Now, we may take our rightful place within the collective consciousness because we understand how it feels and can relate that feeling to others.

Our emotional health relies on and affects our relationships. We may seek partners who have a script that is a mirror reversal of our own, hoping we can resolve the pain of old wounds from their or our childhood and adulthood. Each of us has intentionally put to sleep or is unconscious of certain parts of ourselves. In this state, we dream up fearful imaginings about our intimate partner. In disowning parts of ourselves, we make them "other" or foreign and overreact when we see them in our partner. Most serious relationship conflicts are fueled by this kind of projection. It is expressed by recoiling in an exaggerated way. If one is afraid of one's own anger, just the thought of our partner's possible anger will feel overwhelming. If one can't stand one's own needs, this makes one claustrophobic. Reacting to a partner's anger or need by pushing that person away comes from our fear of experiencing those feelings. In this way, the inner struggle turns into an outer struggle with the partner. Anger has a huge effect on our skin. Being in an angry relationship is detrimental because it affects the production of endorphins that create our inner and outer glow.

In some strange way, our larger intelligence is what draws this paradox together with an inner knowledge and hope that we can help each other heal old wounds and recover the important missing pieces of ourselves. Yet, the healing cannot occur as long as the two see each other as the source of fear rather than the source of resolution. When they choose the second course, couples can awaken from old scripted behaviors and address their needs and fears, developing a stronger connection. Our mothers may have communicated that our partners affect our social standing and ability to raise children, but they may not have known or mentioned how they can affect our beauty from the inside out. Our appearance can change as we change our partners: we adapt to match their traits. Even adopted children take on traits of their adoptive parents.

Again, we continue to press on the idea of awareness, awakening, and self-care for healing and living. Only when we become honest with ourselves do we become vulnerable, and only when we are vulnerable do we reach out for spiritual strength. That is when we truly become strong and complete and our integrity starts to take part in our actions.

To me, there are two main components to true happiness: honesty and gratitude. Honesty is the place you start with yourself and others. Being honest keeps you solid and stable; it affords you peace. Gratitude allows you to find happiness in the place you are at and will stop you from losing that place. Gratitude will expand your life and allow you to reach your potential.

Kinesiology is a discipline proven to be very helpful in addressing emotional health issues from energetic and hereditary sources.

It has the ability to identify and eliminate the old opinions and belief systems that are no longer serving you. This technique eliminates the obstacles from your life and replaces them with those that create harmony and happiness in your life.

Seasonal Tip:

Ask yourself if the reason you are attracted to a relationship could ever become the reason you would walk away from it in the future.

Digesting Emotions

It is obvious we need physical food, but we also need spiritual food. There is a relationship between the amount of physical food we eat and the amount of non-material food we consume. One offsets the other. This balance affects our perception of the immediate environment and the scope in which we can reach other levels. Physical and material foods are consumed through our mouth; non-material foods are absorbed through our nervous system and meridians. We must have both in order to be spiritually sound. Awareness and flow with our environment reveal this simple path to self-care.

Our behaviors do affect ourselves and others. Knowing this, we must first balance ourselves in order to achieve healthy relationships. When you think of emotions and how they can affect those close

147

to us, consider insecurity. It is one of those emotions that can do incredible damage. It can affect the heart and the reproductive organs and create diseases. Jealousy is an unhealthy representation of insecurity and greed. When we are calm and in rhythm with life, these emotional states do not frequent or dominate our thoughts or behaviors.

Our spirit is represented by the endocrine system that consists of the pituitary gland, thyroid, thymus, digestive organs, and reproductive organs. Imbalance that happens in the pituitary glands affect hormone production and our thoughts. If hormones are not produced regularly, they can cause an imbalance in women's menstrual cycles and an emotional imbalance in men. Both will experience effects in their digestive systems. The digestive organs consist of the adrenal gland, spleen, pancreas, gall bladder, liver, kidneys, and intestine. Any imbalance here can cause bile and gastrointestinal disorders. Constant GI disorders weaken the sensory ability of the intestine and its messaging to our brain. As you can see, our emotional health is closely responsible for our digestion and our weight. Greed, as a governing emotion, can cause excessive weight. On the other hand, giving away too much of anything, including abandoning oneself, can cause one to become underweight. The brain tells our body to make cells. When we have emotional or physical problems, this messaging is not taking place. This is why people can deteriorate so rapidly in health with the loss of or separation from their loved one(s). The emotional distress affects the bodily functions. This helps us understand how real the words "love sick" truly are. This is why people feel they could die from loss of love: they really can if they do not take care of themselves. Physiologically, what is happening to them is that toxins from grief are being released into their liver. Love, on the other hand, activates all strands of DNA, the pituitary gland, and the thyroid, promoting a healthy metabolism, releasing happy hormones (endorphins), and providing clarity of thought. Feelings of love, peace, and kindness create high vibrations that touch our genetic codes and those around us. Self-confidence keeps the digestive organs healthy. Awakening these qualities keeps a person's digestion balanced.

Happiness is expressed in us through beauty. Happy people appear more beautiful. Their energy and vitality overflow and their best attributes shine through.

Emotional Retention

A sign of emotionally holding back can manifest in physiological processes in the form of constipation, edema, allergies, indigestion, cramping, headaches, gall bladder disease, kidney stones, and excess weight. Emotional clutter is revealed in every aspect of your body, and these signs exhibit emotional stagnation that needs to be addressed and released. Holding on to negative emotions can age you at a faster rate than letting them go. It will rob you of your ageless longevity.

Our breath carries the expression of our emotion without words. It is part of our body language. Our unconscious breathing patterns also reveal our emotions and state of mind. Once we learn to read our own breathing patterns, we will be able to address our emotions and their source. The physical part will follow through a change of posture and attitude. This will lead us to the source in order to address it and eliminate the stress or illness; it will apply to all factors in our lives once we choose to self-evaluate and self-heal. Use your breath as your guide.

Seasonal Tip:

Use your breath to release your emotions, self-soothe, and become present. Be aware of your own patterns.

Love Aspect

Having love in your life is a matter of survival and longevity. We can see love mirrored in the eyes of those who love us, and we learn to respond and create love by mirroring it back. This conduit is energy and it releases hormones in your body. In order to accept love, we have to accept that we are worthy of it, and each of us is. Anyone can have love in their lives and so can you. A pet, a well-cared-for plant, a lover, a child, a mentor, a friend–any of these can offer you more for your emotional health than something you can buy in a store or design on your own.

The act of growing things supports our emotional health. It has been proven over and over that taking children or pets into a hospital, senior housing, or assisted living environment motivates people to engage more fully in their own lives. When someone feels love or compassion for other living things, then that person's own vitality increases. We can do this daily as we feed our emotional hunger and strive for well-being. It is an integral part of our survival.

Experiencing a sense of love without an assigned recipient or giver shows a healthy state of mind and contentment within a person. We can feel love as a state of mind, just as we feel any other feelings. It is time to lose the misconception that love only exists during a relationship.

Love is the same as all of the other feelings we process and can come and go based on our exposure to daily events.

Photo by Liza Gershman

Wear clothes that are appropriate for the occasion.

Wearing comfortable and natural fabrics is soothing on our skin. Binding clothing that does not fit can make us irritable and snappy throughout the day.

Clothes allow us to express our mood on a daily basis. In some cases, they provide the confidence that is essential to perform tasks. At other times, they allow us to be respectful by wearing appropriate clothing.

Some good examples of this are wardrobes worn to the performance arts. I wish that jeans were never worn to the opera, symphony, and ballet. The artists spend their entire lives achieving the skill to give a flawless performance for our enjoyment, yet, some find it too difficult to be well-groomed or properly attired when attending a performance. Arts, by definition, are a gift to all of us, and very few have the gift to be the very best. I feel that by being well-dressed at cultural events shows support, respect, and gratitude for all the effort that goes into practicing and organizing the performances. In addition, putting time into getting ready for the event just may heighten the experience itself.

Our attire plays an important role in our society and for our well-being. This can be more important for some than others based on the season and their senses.

Many factors affect our emotional well-being. Our diet, exercise, herbal care, and breath help us to stabilize during emotional times. They support our physical health and help us navigate emotional turmoil with empathy for experiences with friends, family, and loved ones. Using the appropriate seasonal fabrics against your skin will keep you feeling fresh, calm, and present in your daily life.

Choosing the right seasonal fabrics is a large part of seasonal life. When you combine these with colors, your entire closet will be different. It is a very good way to bring exciting change without long travels.

I hope that by seeing how our wardrobe plays a role in our daily experience, maybe having a few extra things in the closet is not a waste after all. We all need some adventure.

Meditation, the Controlled Breath

There are many forms of meditation; perhaps you have heard of them, and maybe you have avoided them. It is time to start paying attention to your needs as a form of self-communication and self-preservation. It is not accidental that meditation has been practiced and encouraged for optimal health for centuries. It is an ancient, healing tool.

When I End My Day

Before I fall asleep in bed, I spend a few quiet minutes with myself. I want a moment to go into my closure-of-the-day meditation. It may take a few seconds or a few minutes. It depends on the activities of the day. I allow those moments to be truthful in assessing my actions and my satisfaction with them and determining if I could have done anything differently. This is my time to be open with myself and take note of my alignment with my intentions. Knowing what a great part of our lives breathing holds, I encourage everyone to use a few deep and mindful breaths before falling asleep.

The Law of Opposites

In nature, most poisons have an antidote. All of our solutions and cures can be found in natural environments all over the world thatwe now have access to. This balance shows us that everything created in nature is perfect. The best way of testing it and convincing ourselves of this is by applying muscle testing from the discipline of kinesiology, which has only recently gained acknowledgement and become commonly used.

One Minute of Introspection

Photo by Elaine Foo

There are several ways to create a relaxed, self-soothing moment to add a positive spin on your daily outlook or goal setting. Start this by creating a statement of intention.

You can induce a deep, quiet, focused state in just one minute. I like to place my hands together so the fingers are touching, activating **touch sense,** and then I press them firmly to connect with

157

ELISABETH THIERIOT

each other.

- ❖ Lie or sit comfortably in a quiet place to activate **heart sense**.

- ❖ Place your fingertips together and gently press to activate **touch sense**.

- ❖ Close your eyes activating **sound sense**.

- ❖ Take deep breaths through your nose and exhale slowly through your mouth for a 10-count to activate **smell sense**.

- ❖ Imagine between your palms in the space created by your fingers touching that there is a whole world for you.

- ❖ Press gently to feel the world in your palms.

- ❖ Imagine it full and contained because it is yours.

- ❖ Imagine the harder you press, the more you can feel the perimeter of your world.

- ❖ Count to 60 slowly.

- ❖ Release your fingers and allow your suggestion to come into your mind. Repeat it slowly over and over in rhythm…
  "I feel amazing. I am so grateful for all that I have. I am

158

energetic and successful. I am feeling loving and kind…
my intentions are aligned with my ethics and my goals."

❖ Imagine the results of your feeling and its expression
   outward and inward. Visualize the image to activate
   visual sense.

❖ Feel the vision.

❖ After a few moments, allow yourself to come back, feeling
   refreshed and centered for a powerful day.

❖ Engage in the act of swallowing to activate your **taste sense**
   before you open your eyes and get on with your day.

You have now successfully reset all your senses!

CHAPTER SEVEN

RENEWAL AND REPAIR:

THE ESSENTIAL VALUE OF SLEEP

Treat Your Bed and Your Sheets Like a Sanctuary for Your Body and Your Sleep

The quality of the sheets we sleep in is just as important as our sleep because it affects the level of repair we get, due to the effect the sheets have on our skin. Invest in beautiful sheets and make your bed a place of comfort and rejuvenation. When our skin is at peace during sleep, our bodies can rest because irritable stimulation is absent. It is undeniable that it feels different to wrap ourselves in soft cotton, linen, or cashmere than it does in nylon or a synthetic, rough material. Our bodies can tell which fabrics were once alive and which were not. If possible, change your sheets every three days.

We Repair During Sleep

In sleep, our body engages in cellular repair and rebuilding. Our vital energy is directed to assimilate and distribute our daily intake of nutrients and proteins. This is for the purposes of hormonal production and storage, eradicating inflammations, lymphatic drainage, muscle fiber building, and our overall preparation to detoxify during morning hours. This is why sleep cannot be omitted.

During sleep, organs like the liver and kidneys detoxify the daily accumulation of ingested, inhaled, or absorbed toxins. These processes are much more active and efficient while sleeping. Protein synthesis repair and restoration also occurs during sleep periods. We can assist in this repair more quickly and efficiently with seasonal care and botanical herbs. Research shows that the skin is far more receptive to topical preparations that are applied while we sleep.

Feeling tired is a signal from our body to shut down and recoup our system. When we sleep, we go into parasympathetic mode. In other words, we are on auto-pilot. When people are sick, we find them sleeping far more than normal. When we are traveling, our sleep is irregular at first because it is shared between our daily obligations and our bodily needs. Our muscles can perform all of the time, but it is our brain that needs the shutdown time the most. It is only during our sleep that we are able to repair our daily damage; it is also the only time when our brain runs a scan of what we need and what we have, allowing the immune system to restore and utilize all acquired nutrients and wisdom from our daily intake.

Sleep is essential to our rejuvenation processes and maintaining cognitive skills, such as speech, memory, innovation, and flexible thinking. It is also essential to brain development and information retrieval. Lack of sleep is a serious problem in our society, but you will have much more success in achieving the sleep you need when you adopt a seasonal living philosophy. As a result, you will feel more in tune, and your productivity will be so much better and more effective. When you feel at ease, you will feel more confident, and success will come more easily.

Getting quality sleep is imperative to your health and well-being. Serotonin directs sleep, calmness, and emotional tranquility. Dopamine directs shallow sleep, irritability, arousal, and emotional anxiety. Sleep deprivation can produce psychosis and paranoia as well.

Placing a green live plant in the bedroom provides needed oxygen during sleep.

The Work of the Unconscious

In the not so distant past, common medical knowledge told us that sleep was a period of brain inactivity. Since then, research has shown us that the brain remains active during sleep. There is a progressive decrease in the activity of most neurons in the brain as sleep progresses; our patterns of neuron activity change from random patterns during wakefulness to coordinated and parallel patterns during non-REM sleep. These stabilizing factors that occur while physiological demands are reduced and temperature and blood pressure drop indicate our body is in a meditative process, no less powerful than the healing ability of meditation. Medications, behaviors, and varied lifestyle choices influence when and how well we sleep, as does our environment, food, nutrition, water, and self-care. When we sleep, the entire brain is involved, although, it processes differently during active sleep stages, and this is validated by current research on sleep at the **Stanford Sleep Center** and the **National Institute of Neurological Disorders and Stroke,** as well as many others.

Circadian Rhythm

Your circadian rhythm, the body's 24-hour internal clock, regulates hormones, energy production, and cognitive brain skills. Our natural body rhythms regulate our daily internal cycles. When they fall out of sync, you may experience the symptoms of Seasonal Affective Disorder (SAD).

Without proper morning light, our body clocks don't produce the hormones we need to wake up and feel active. A lack of daylight means we'll have less energy and be less productive. When we stay up excessively late we then create mood problems, alter our hormonal production, have weight issues, and lower our activity level. It is all regulated by our internal body clock.

Seasonal Tip:

When you are tired, take note and get rest, even if it is only for a few minutes. Eating when fatigued can slow down digestion, cause weight gain, and become toxic.

Lack of Sleep Can Cause Toxicity

Studies clearly show that a lack of sleep can cause toxicity and malnutrition. We all need a specific amount of sleep, particular to our bodies, for these processes to take place. Circadian Disorders often make the sufferer feel out of step with normal waking and sleeping hours. Our brain needs sleep in order to maintain its coherence and ability to retrieve information.

Our organs need their time to go through detox and repair while we sleep. A lack of sleep prevents these processes from taking place, creating a buildup of toxins that may lead to illness.

Sleep Aids

Our bodies need at least 20 minutes of physical activity each day, whether by walking or in some other form. This is essential to having restful sleep. Our brains need to obtain sufficient information from daylight to gauge a shutdown of the system for the circadian night cycle. While sleeping, we assimilate information acquired during the day.

Chamomile has been used for centuries as an herbal sleep aid, and it also has a positive effect on digestion. It is a very gentle herb and considered safe both for adults and children[2]. As an herb for insomnia, it is most often taken as a tea or tonic. It has a mild flavor and soothing effect that aids sleep, reduces restlessness, and can decrease anxiety.

Honey is used for greater recovery when healing or from stress.

Supplements such as tryptophan, melatonin, calcium, and magnesium can be obtained from supplements or by eating foods that contain them.

- ❖ **Spring**— Half of this season should be split between winter and summer sleep patterns, as it is considered a transitional period.

- ❖ **Summer**— Summer is the time to take afternoon naps, because the longer days can deprive you of much-needed

---

[2] Pregnant and nursing women should not consume chamomile as it can cause uterine contractions.

sleep. Go to sleep with the sunset and rise early with sunrise. This way, you can achieve the same amount of sleep needed for your body to repair.

- ❖ **Autumn**— Half of this season should be split between winter and summer sleep patterns, as it is considered a transitional period. Extra calcium can support our sleep, relaxing us so we can sleep longer. Obtaining deeper sleep and allowing the natural process of nutrient retention and accumulation is especially important in the autumn.

- ❖ **Winter**— Do not take naps; as the sun rises later, we tend to have more quiet evening times than any other time during the year. Going to bed earlier is advised.

While we sleep, our body temperature is regulated by changing blood flow to our skin and that can result in shivering and sweating. Our breathing evens out and becomes steady, requiring the least amount of regulation and effort as the body works on repair processes. To aid this process, it is best to sleep without clothes, as the body will maintain an even temperature from your toes to the top of your head. It's one less thing for the brain to monitor while you are sleeping.

Seasonal Tip:

Make adjustments to your sleeping environment. Open windows in summer, add warmer fabrics in winter, have a cup of herbal tea before bedtime, and get a good night's sleep in every season.

Burn Fat While You Sleep

Yes, you really can and do burn fat while you sleep. Our body can't hold all the nutrients in the summer; that's our body's most expanded state where anything that goes in, goes out. Brown cells are our body's backup resource. We first use up energy from food, and when that is exhausted during the night, we begin to use the energy from the brown cells. Brown cells are fat-burning cells. As we sleep, the energy from brown cells, as well as all the nutrients that are collected and held by them, are released. Scientists would like people to create more brown cells to fight obesity, since white cells are not easily converted to fuel or to store toxins. People with a healthy diet have higher levels of brown cells.

SAD (Seasonal Affective Disorder)

As the evenings lengthen, the increased darkness can bring on seasonal gloom. While light summer mornings and warm evenings can bring us cheerful energy, the opposite happens with the shorter periods of light in the winter. Many people find it hard to function optimally, and some have an incredible sense of depression. Sleep during this stage can be erratic, and this can cause more damage than just the emotional state. It becomes essential that we take the necessary measures to keep ourselves comfortable and in balance.

Internal Organs Function on a Biological Clock

Each body organ is related to specific hours of the day and night, but it is individually based on your primary sense and the time of the year. The information below is general with regard to "time," but relevant with regard to flow and process.

5 a.m. – 7 a.m. Large Intestine

This is when blood flow concentrates in the large intestines, which are responsible for elimination. It is beneficial to train your body to take advantage of this peak time because it is more efficient. There is an emotional connection to this process, and it can be translated into feeling stuck or experiencing grief, which can become physically manifested. If you find yourself feeling grumpy at such hours, you may be grieving about something or you might be frustrated with something in your life at the moment.

7 a.m. – 9 a.m. Stomach

Digestive function is optimal at this time. The stomach is linked to the emotion of worry, and significant physical or emotional changes may relate to stomach-linked emotion and digestive function.

9 a.m. – 11 a.m. Spleen

The spleen and pancreas are the only organs that rebuild and replace themselves if damaged. It has an important digestive function. Like the stomach, the spleen is also linked to worry, overwork, overthinking, and general excessive mental exertion. Physical problems at this hour, particularly problems in digestion, can relate to these emotional factors.

11 a.m. – 1 p.m. Heart

The emotions of the heart are joy, enthusiasm, and restfulness.

This means the heart is made stronger with these emotions and hindered by their opposites. Any physical problem at this time, such as aches, pains, or energy dips, may be linked with blockages in feeling your heart's full joy. The heart has an aversion to heat. In many hot countries, a siesta is taken in these hours. It also indicates that going for a heat-inducing run during heart hours is not recommended for optimal heart health.

1 p.m. – 3 p.m. Small Intestine

When the small intestine is at optimal performance, it is the best time to eat your first meal of the day. The emotion linked with the small intestine is joy.

3 p.m. – 5 p.m. Bladder

The bladder is linked to fear and anger. Physical signs of discomfort or any abnormal symptoms at this time could relate to this emotion. Salty foods or seawater can strengthen the bladder, so drinking a cup of savory soup with added sea salt, replenishing by drinking **Replete Aqua™**, or spraying **Replete Rejuvenating Mist™** on our skin would be beneficial at this time.

5 p.m. – 7 p.m. Kidney

The kidney is the body organ most strongly linked to fear. Not only are physical manifestations at these times possibly related to experiencing fear, (i.e., becoming weak in the knees) but also it is best to avoid things that might cause fear because they can weaken the kidney. A good example of this is watching scary movies. The kidney is closely linked with willpower, security, feelings of aloofness, and isolation. Like the bladder, the kidney is strengthened by salty foods or **Replete Aqua**™ deep ocean water.

7 p.m. – 9 p.m. Pericardium

This may be associated with good circulation and peak reproductive function. Since the pericardium is closely linked to the heart, it is also associated with joy.

9 p.m. – 11 p.m. Triple Warmer

This is not actually an organ in western medicine; it is a meridian defined by its function, which is to circulate energy throughout the other organs. It is also linked to joy.

11 p.m. – 1 a.m. Gall Bladder

The gall bladder is linked to courage and the use of wise judgment. The gall bladder runs along a similar meridian to the liver meridian. Signs and symptoms arising at these hours, such as nausea, can relate to problems with making decisions, shyness, and timidity.

1 a.m. – 3 a.m. Liver

Since the liver meridian overlaps the gall bladder meridian, it becomes activated by the gall bladder processes. The emotion linked most strongly to the liver is anger. The liver's function is to remove and detoxify the body of chemicals and negative emotions. Although frustration, bitterness, and resentment are also closely linked. It is best to be asleep during these hours to allow maximal energy to be diverted. This explains why an early night's sleep is congruent with a healthy body and mind. If you find yourself waking up in this time of night or in a period that should be dedicated to sleep, it may be linked to feelings of latent anger or frustration that are overwhelming in the process of regaining your healthy state.

3 a.m. – 5 a.m. Lungs

If you find yourself waking for no apparent reason during the lungs' hours, it may be linked to grief, the main lung emotion. It is not uncommon to have these feelings during these hours. Similarly, if you're already awake and experience sudden changes in energy or well-being, it may be related to grief and detachment. Feeling serene at these hours could indicate having strong lungs and a strong voice in life. The lungs govern the voice, respiratory system, sweat glands, skin health, and immune system health, so recharging the lungs with sleep is particularly important if you have issues in any of these areas.

Cyclical Rhythms

It may sound unfamiliar, but if you stop to think about these marked times and your own experiences, you are bound to find a correlation with how we feel and function. It is also interesting to note that this knowledge dates back to around 350 B.C., and has been retained for many, many centuries. There is a repetitious structure showing up through civilizations and cultures: the medicine wheel, the clock, the biological clock, circadian rhythms, crop rotation, the circle of life, the planets, the solar system, the planetary alignment, the organ clock, and on and on…

This was an independent occurrence among widespread civilizations. It is a phenomenon of how they recognized and utilized the same rhythms and patterns. A good example of repeated patterns and presence of higher knowledge are pyramids built by Aztecs, Mayans, and Egyptians of the same pattern, of the same accuracy, at the same time. How could this be? Isn't it obvious that there is more to consider than what we touch and see in our immediate world?

Recurring events build patterns and create complex systems. They noticed that all is expanding; therefore, the cycles move in the spiral pattern that expands with movement and time.

Each cyclical rhythm is responsible for the success of a greater pattern: those affecting us and everything around us.

Everything is connected and codependent. When one cycle is not completed, other functions fail to ignite.

The entire Mayan civilization recognized the impact of natural cycles and their cause and effect on their lifestyles, quality of life, and health. They implemented the patience into observation of all naturally occurring cycles. They used them to be proactive in benefitting from the natural cycles or preventing devastation. They had an awareness of connectedness between all living elements, which led to the creation of the most precise calendar in existence. For example, by crossing over sciences, they engineered the first underground filtered and pressurized water system that withstood times of flood, drought, and high winds carrying debris and delivered clear mineralized cool water into their homes. They understood that progress is made by taking into account aspects of all sciences, gathered in recorded observations, through cause and effect, which equaled a specific outcome.

The Cycle of 23

These are a few of the known cycles to us so far. This number returns to us again and again throughout history.

- ❖ The number 23 is often related to death.

- ❖ In the I-Ching, hexagram 23 is named Splitting Apart. In the chromosome sequence, the split that comes before joining with another set of 23 chromosomes becomes a new embryo.

- ❖ There are 23 chromosomes in the human reproductive cells.

- ❖ A fetus starts to produce white blood cells from their own bone marrow at 23 weeks.

❖ When a fetus is 23 weeks along, the lower areas of the lungs form and air sacs develop.

❖ It takes 23 seconds for blood to circulate through the human body.

❖ Our DNA pattern shows irregular connections at every 23rd section.

❖ The small intestine is approximately 23 feet long in adults.

❖ The axis of the earth is 23.45 degrees.

❖ Euclidean geometry contains 23 axioms, and the number 23 itself adds up to five, which is a prime component in the base 10 of mathematics.

❖ Solar cycle 23: The sun's magnetism changes, affecting weather patterns.

❖ The human arm has 23 points of articulation.

❖ A day and night rotation of the earth is more than 23 hours, but less than 24, which is the reason we have leap year.

This part of the Cistine Chapel ceiling shows God's finger bringing the divine spark to Adam. Across and that of another, travels as much meaning as is contained in all the books of the world— travels the essence of life.

—Loretta Pratt Bolin, M.D.

Seasonal Tip:

Make a list of things you considered a coincidence. Notice you are not alone in thinking the same thing. Act from the place that all things are connected. This will aid in your sense of organization and awareness.

Photo by Ashley Farrah Horowitz

CHAPTER EIGHT

SEASONAL EATING

Your digestion affects your mood. You have the ability improve your digestion with your positive attitude alone. If your digestion is bad, so too will be your mood. Make an effort to smile and keep your food intake within your body's ability to digest.

Modern science is wonderful for saving lives, but it's often not wonderful for maintaining the quality of life. We should all make our food purchasing decisions based on our desire for improving our lives and making them more beautiful by being healthy and energetic.

Avoid buying foods and products that are processed or have multiple ingredients or items you cannot identify. When shopping, avoid areas in the store that are full of bright packaging and promises.

Don't be in a hurry when cooking! Microwaving destroys the water and minerals in food, and when that's gone, there's not much nutrition left.

Digestion

Digestion is the key to our survival. Our stomach has specialized regions that evolved into organs as part of a complex digestive organ system. As nutrients are dispersed through the digestive system to reach all the cells in the body, they govern every aspect of our body, our mood and our behavior, our vitality, and our longevity.

The most current deterrent to our longevity is surgery that is commonly performed to remove parts of the intestine that have failed to work properly. This leads to a progressive loss of nutrients and accelerates the decline in one's quality of life. All this is simply because medical science has failed to look for the natural way of restoring intestinal function through the use of ocean water as a remedy (for colitis, irritable bowel syndrome, impacted colon, etc.). Each inch of our digestive tract is necessary. It has an assigned function in the process of digestion and assimilating of the nutrients needed for our existence. Losing the balance by cutting out parts of the digestive tract leads to a slow and certain insidious systemic breakdown. The key to survival is our ability to adapt to whatever the current sources of nutrients may be. Having our full intestinal and digestive tract is essential. The evolution of most species is first attributed to digestive tract changes and adaptation.

Meal Time

What we say and how we communicate with the outside world is equally important as the environment at the table while we eat. Always eat in peace. Keep unpleasant topics away from the table. For our emotional and mental health, food must enter our bodies in peace to be utilized most effectively. Saying something insensitive or unkind to a person can have a physical effect, particularly before or during a meal. This is why I can't stress enough the importance of keeping negative conversations and negative energy away from the table at mealtimes. When we become upset before or during a meal, it upsets our digestion. When we touch our food, we connect with it and the organs in our body start to respond. We should take our time during our meals, making sure to cut our food into smaller bites and chew them fully. It is a good time to reinforce the way we connect with ourselves and loved ones. See it as a nurturing time for the body and mind.

Limit liquids during meals so as not to dilute your body's digestive ability. Even drinking water after a meal should be put off. Water dilutes digestive function from the moment it enters your mouth. Limiting liquids will also keep the size of your stomach small, not stretched with liquids and food all at once. Observing 4 - 6 hours between meals is necessary for the proper absorption of food in our digestive tract and having digestive enzymes ready for the meal.

Seasonal Tip:

Allow at least three hours after eating before going to sleep. This will keep your face from swelling and stretching the next morning.

We rely on bacteria to fully break down our food and make it usable for full assimilation in our bodies. Our body stores active enzymes in an inactive state, ready to step-up for the next meal. Maintaining this functionality is critical to our absorption of nutrients that keep us youthful. When you run out of proenzyme, it becomes more difficult to assimilate food and can make you prone to allergic reactions and indigestion. This is the reason I recommend breaks of 4 - 6 hours between meals as it sets aside time for the proenzymes to rebuild.

Emotional Effect on Digestion

Psychological imbalances follow a natural order. For example, how you feel affects your digestion and sense of well-being. Positive feelings are alkaline-forming and provide a sense of strength and energy. Negative feelings create acidity and cause a loss of energy or fatigue. Both of these emotional states also affect the digestion and your body's ability to assimilate nutrients from your food. For this reason, I stress keeping meal times peaceful, enjoyable, and positive.

Food Combinations

I talk about food combining because the combination of foods we eat becomes a factor in our digestion. Our digestion and ability to process foods affect our skin, other organs, our sense of well-being, and our energy level. In fact, digestion is one of the biggest factors in longevity. It is also a factor in the growth of cancers; many internal cancers will communicate their presence through our skin. The following are rules I observe that have served me very well.

Grains should only be combined with **fresh fruits, dry fruits**, and other **carbohydrates,** in addition to **root** and **leafy vegetables**. They can be fine combined with dairy products; even so, I believe that past puberty, we do best to abstain from dairy altogether.

Dairy requires specific enzymes to break down milk protein, as well as the commonly talked about lactose. Many of us do not have the necessary digestive enzyme once we enter adulthood. Beyond lactose intolerance is the issue of breaking down the protein. This digestive issue can lead to extended abdomen and back pain as a result.

Dairy can cause a multitude of health issues, from colitis to fibroids, malnutrition due to mucus in the lining of large and small intestine, chronic sinus conditions, hearing loss due to constant ear congestions, and infections. Dairy can have delayed reactions on the body and cause severe headaches. The first could happen within the first three days after consumption, the second type 60 - 90 days after consumption. In the latter case, your body does not have the proper tools to break down dairy products, so it just leaves them in your system to deal with later. Between 60 - 90 days, the remaining dairy protein is released, and you may get severe headaches. This usually happens on a light-food day when your body goes into a detox mode. This type of intestinal condition can cause anxiety, depression, and feeling out of sorts for what seems to be no apparent reason.

Butter in clarified form is an exception to the avoidance of dairy in my diet and can be used on all grains and proteins to cook with or spiced on.

Beans are a good source of protein for some, and you should **combine six or more types together** when cooking them. This way, they are easier to digest and utilize by our system.

Meat and fish should never be combined with fruits and dairy, as they require the opposite type of digestive enzymes. Meats, fish, and eggs are best digested and assimilated when served and cooked with leafy vegetables and fats.

Much of what I am saying here, regarding the timing and quantities, needs to be guided by each individual's needs and the resulting observations. You must be in tune with yourself to increase or decrease the amount of nutrients you are obtaining from your diet. No one will know more or better than you as to the effect it has on your daily living and health.

Corresponding Fruits and Vegetables to Our Organ Needs

Photo by Deva Sexton

Walnuts resemble the brain, and are good for it too.

Certain fruits and plants resemble and support specific organs in the human body.

When you look at a tree and its root system, it is equivalent to the way the lungs appear and their importance to their host organism. Take walnuts, for example; they look exactly like our brain and they are good brain food. It is not a coincidence that the foods grown during each season supplement the organ functions most needed during the same time of year. The key to living well is to acknowledge, learn, and accept this idea, connect with it, and actualize it for yourself.

When you fail to care for your body—consider what you put on your skin or expose yourselves to—or fail to tune into seasonal living, your emotional and physical health will suffer. You will pay the toll sooner by shortening your life and decreasing your enjoyment while living. Our bodies react and develop problems when there is a lack of attention to their needs.

You Can Rebuild Your DNA by Supplementing With Trace Nutrients

As any organism ages, it can lose efficiency. With mineral supplementing, we can bring our systems back into balance, reverse aging, and minimize the risk of diseases such as diabetes, hypoglycemia, dehydration, gout, and any disease caused by toxins.

We need all of the available minerals to function, but some minerals are essential to restoring function and balance. Here are a few examples of imbalance in the following table.

SYMPTOM	CAUSES	MINERAL DEFICIENCY or EXCESS	BENEFITS OF SUPPLEMEN- TING
Anxiety, agitation, Sleep disorders, irritability, abnormal heart rhythms, depression (and many more).	Diabetes, IBS, pancreatitis, hyperthyroidism, kidney disease. Too much; coffee, rock salt, or alcohol.	**Magnesium deficiency** All our organs, especially the heart, muscles, and kidneys need magnesium	Activates enzymes, contributes to energy production, helps regulate the levels of calcium, copper, zinc, vitamin D, potassium, as well as other minerals in the body.
Symptoms are subtle: chronic viral infections, dandruff, fluid on inner ear, high cholesterol, heart disease, compromised immune system, rheumatoid arthritis.	Alcohol, birth control pills, smoking, Crohn's disease or ulcerative colitis.	**Selenium deficiency**	Works as an antioxidant, especially when combined with Vitamin E. May activate tumor-suppressing genes. Pairs with iodine to make necessary thyroid hormones.
Sluggishness or fatigue, dry skin, weight gain, sensitivity to temperature changes (symptoms of low thyroid hormone levels) Goiter (enlarged thyroid gland).	Lack of source of key nutrients from natural foods and seaweeds.	**Iodine deficiency** (unlikely to occur in developed countries)	Supplementing is not usually necessary. Any deficiency has a tremendous negative effect on our thyroid, which can quickly lead to serious and long-term, health effects.
Infertility, bone malformation, seizures, and weakness.	Eating too many refined grains.	**Manganese deficiency**	Essential for bone health. Easily obtained from eating whole grains

On a related note, the addition of fluoride to the water supply or in other products can actually be harmful to our health. In 2010, *Time Magazine* cited fluoride as one of the top 10 common household toxins. At the current allowable amount in drinking water in the U.S., fluoride blocks the absorption of iodine, which can negatively affect thyroid function. Iodine is essential to our function and reproduction.

Another harmful contaminant mineral is aluminum, which can be found almost everywhere in our environment. It's in everything from cookware, storage products, and canned beverages to underarm antiperspirant/deodorant. Cooking food in aluminum foil can increase its absorption by up to 378%, and using foil for storing acidic foods increases absorption too. To keep you from accumulating this harmful toxin, which some studies link to Alzheimer's disease and osteoporosis, you can take calcium, zinc, and magnesium. Alternative remedies are lemon juice, turmeric, garlic, kelp, and cilantro. It's almost impossible to remove aluminum from our surroundings these days, but with awareness of its prevalence, you'll be a step ahead.

Proteins

Proteins are a component of the building blocks of our bodies and used to grow or repair cells. While they are the primary constituents of blood, enzymes, cellular fluids, and hormones, they are used for body construction versus energy production. Amino acids are components of proteins, and eight of the 22 amino acids can only be found in foods. If one essential amino acid is missing, the body can only make a limited amount of usable protein. A seasonal approach contains plenty of the essential amino acids and allows the body to process more naturally and put all the energy in the right places.

Carbohydrates

Carbohydrates are the body's source of energy. How they are absorbed is what differentiates them. We discern how quickly they become usable by the time of day you consume them and your system. Although the FDA has come out with the glycemic index to help control blood sugar levels, your best guide is your own body. Your levels may vary from hour to hour and day to day. It is essential that you notice what you eat and the effect it has on your body. These effects are based more on each individual's system than on any glycemic index. When you notice how your body reacts to foods and processes sugar levels, you can prevent bloodsugar spikes, energy spikes, and fatigue. However, if you avoid carbohydrates altogether, your face will become drawn and lifeless. You need the carbohydrates to put fresh energy into your skin cells. The absence of carbohydrates is visible on your face.

Carbohydrates can be eaten alone or combined as cooked grains or air popped/puffed; limit baked carbohydrates.

Some low glycemic index (good) carbohydrates are beans, small seeds, most whole intact grains, most vegetables, most sweet fruits, and fructose.

High glycemic index (avoid or limit) foods are white bread, most white rice, corn flakes, most extruded breakfast cereals, maltose, glucose, potatoes (they can vary extensively, even within the same variety), and pretzels.

The four types of carbohydrates that become sugars are the following:

❖ Glucose—found in grains and vegetables

❖ Fructose—found in fruits

❖ Lactose—milk and dairy

❖ Sucrose—cane and beets

We need complex carbohydrates in the form of glucose or fruits and vegetables to support our physical activity throughout the day. While we metabolize them, our activity is sustained.

Eat some cucumbers in the afternoon with a pinch of sea salt; it will help to stabilize your blood sugar level.

Fats

Fat consumption in straight format is much more common in prosperous countries than in other countries. What this really means is that fats are more common where prepared foods are eaten more frequently. Excessive volumes of proteins and carbohydrates tend to be stored as fats in various areas of the body and can have a harmful impact on our internal organ functions. The body needs fat with more intensity in diets that are unbalanced. This is true for some of the Arctic people's diets, for example, where whole grains or greens are not easily accessible; the people need to consume high-fat diets in order to survive.

Seasonal Tip:

When in the mood for dessert, choose the one with the most fruit in it. This will help reduce excesses and maintain a healthy

weight. When I followed the macrobiotic guidelines for years, my weight never fluctuated more than one pound.

Herbs

We also need the assistance of herbs. There is a reason why herbs and botanical plants grow everywhere and we have used them as healing tools for as long as we have existed. Their healing properties and their ability to survive in different seasons speaks for itself.

Seasonal Tip:

Parsley is a great support for our adrenal glands. Dandelion, which grows almost year-round, is a common weed in lawns and great for edema, PMS, bloating, and water retention; it can be taken in tea, eaten in salads, or cooked. Mint is a great digestive. Drinking mint tea sometimes after dinner or adding it as a seasoning to your food are good ways to integrate mint into your diet.

Seasonal Digestive Aids

- ❖ **Spring**— Chives, onions, leeks — Stimulate digestive enzymes, starting with salivary gland. Caution— always dispose of unused onions after cutting; they attract airborne bacteria.

- ❖ **Summer**— Garlic and mint — Help break down animal fats and proteins.

- ❖ **Autumn**— Apples — Aid digestion and assimilation due to their high enzyme content.

- ❖ **Winter**— Rosemary — Helps break down animal fats and proteins.

- ❖ **Year Round**— Ginger is an all-around tonic; it settles upset stomachs. Make a tonic or tea by boiling sliced ginger in water and drinking it hot or cold. Ginger also gives you energy.

For a list of Food Consumption Guidelines, see Appendix A.

My Be Fabulous At Any Age Notes:

Photo by Drew Altizer

CHAPTER NINE

SEASONAL FOOD

Our Food, the Seasonal Antidote

Nature operates according to the principles of "one grain, ten thousand grains." For every seed the Earth receives, it returns thousands. Nature is forever productive and infinitely diverse. In the practice of genetic engineering, ten thousand seeds are sacrificed for every one that comes to market, or "from ten thousand grains, come one grain." Originally, the heirloom seeds that sustained humanity over the centuries cost nothing; they were given freely by nature. Each genetically engineered seed costs $300 million to bring to market. We now face a choice between two opposite views of life, one natural, the other artificial. The health and happiness of future generations, indeed the health and happiness of all species, could well depend upon which of these two paths we choose.

—Ed Esko

As we begin to wind down in the autumn and adjust to this change, bodies and cells also contract to hold in the vitamins and nutrients we gained in the summer months. Autumn is a powerful season, dictating that our bodies prepare for cold weather and the lack of fresh fruits in the winter by bringing us some of the most intensely flavored fruits and vegetables. Take the persimmon, for example, which is as rich in iron as a steak, or pumpkin seeds, which clear the intestine of parasites from eating summer's raw foods. We even get a little bonus with tomatoes at the end of summer for healing our heart from summer romance by gently removing the inner lining to erase the memory of heartbreak.

Food Is Medicine

Tea is an excellent antioxidant.

Photo by Liza Gershman

Having particular foods plays a part in our creation, affecting our growth and development from birth and before. Once we leave the oceanic environment of the womb, we are dependent on outside sources for our health. That is why nature has provided it for us. When we need healing, we can access the sources through natural means. When we consume according to our needs, we will have the following:

❖ Greater energy, better sleep.

❖ Better health and freedom from sickness.

❖ Weight maintenance.

❖ Deep, restorative sleep.

❖ Better memory and moods.

❖ Clarity of thinking.

❖ Fewer mood swings.

❖ Control over personal destiny.

❖ Less reactivity from anger.

❖ Greater empathy and generosity.

❖ One truth with the world and oneself.

❖ Better sexual appetite and more joyful satisfaction.

❖ Joie de Vivre!

The aging process comes about in a variety of ways. Our body runs through cycles regulating its needs and the supply of nutrients it needs to continue life. This means checking current functions of our organs as well, and if a shortage is seen, our body gradually begins the process of shutting down peripheral organs and systems to support the core of life only. This is what aging looks like. When we continually replenish the essential nutrients that run our system, we tend to live longer and retain a higher quality of life. In this sense, we have the power to postpone the aging process. Statistics show that diet has everything to do with our health, which in turn supports our appearance, mood, and success.

To be fabulous, you must feel fabulous: how you feel affects your health and beauty. Be aware of how food makes you feel. Create a personal food list by observing how foods make you feel after you eat them. Include all of the herbs and spices you put on your food as the best way to create your own medicine list too. I combine no more than three spices in each dish, which gives me an easy way to isolate what works and what doesn't.

I personally have found that using food lists I created over time and avoiding foods in the nightshade family (i.e., potatoes, peppers, and eggplant) has worked effectively in the balancing of my own system. This has enabled me to maintain the same weight and energy level throughout my life. I also attribute this to my ever-optimistic view on life and my humorous side, which neverseems to leave, even under the most dreadful situations.

Many areas of the earth where there is large-scale farming have been stripped of the nutrients in the soil. It is recognized that the entire earth is a single, self-regulating ecosystem. Rudolf Steiner offered the first principles of biodynamic farming and gardening as a solution to the issue. This approach is under development in many parts of the world, but it is not enough, as our mineral-depleted soil and its harvest threaten the nutrients we need to sustain healthy lives. We must look outside our immediate environment and supplement our health with vitamins, minerals, and foods.

Since we are now able to acquire foods from remote areas all over the world, we can also find minerals and botanical extracts to replenish our bodies for much-needed repair and maintenance. This way, we can acquire the balanced supply of nutrients no longer easily obtained from food. We can access a variety of roots, bark, stems, leaves, petals, and even mineral-rich ocean waters to match our requirements and protect our bodies from premature aging.

Beneficial Herbs and Plants

Examples of How Herbs or Plants Can Work for You

HERB/PLANT	MEDICINAL USES
Aloe Vera (Aloe barbadensis, A. vera)	A powerful healer for external burns, scrapes, and sunburn and is also helpful as a laxative. In lab tests, aloe-emodin has shown signs of being able to combat leukemia. A European study suggested that its gel can reduce blood sugar levels in diabetics.
Belladonna, Deadly Nightshade, Dwale (Atropa belladonna)	It contains tropane alkaloids, atropine, hyoscamine, and scopolamine, which all have anti-spasmodic, sedative, and narcotic (sleep-inducing or addictive) effects. Doctors use atropine to dilate pupils for eye exams and to treat eye disorders. It numbs nerve endings, can lessen pain when applied locally. The therapeutic amount is very close to the toxic amount.
Brazil Nut (Bertholletia excels)	Amazon rain forest tribes drink tea prepared from the bark of the tree as a remedy for liver ailments. The husks of the seedpods are also administered in a tea to treat stomachaches. Brazil nuts are rich in protein, Vitamin E, and monounsaturated fats. This nut contains approximately 2,500 times as much selenium than other nuts. Selenium has been shown to improve mood and mental functioning and increases blood flow to the brain.

HERB/PLANT	MEDICINAL USES
Cayenne pepper, Red Pepper (Capsicum annuum)	Its active constituent, capsaicin, which produces the heat, can be used to treat pain caused by herpes, arthritis, shingles, rheumatism, and other neuralgias by desensitizing the neurons that transmit pain. It has also been used to treat overactive bladders. Since the 18th century, red pepper has been considered a powerful stimulant and has proved useful in treating many GI and circulatory ailments, especially indigestion. Cayenne may stimulate the release of opiate-like endorphins.
Chocolate, Cocoa, Cacao (Theobroma cacao)	Its primary alkaloid, theobromine, has an effect similar to caffeine, stimulating the muscles, kidneys, and heart. It can also relieve congestion during colds and relaxes the smooth muscle in the digestive tract. Cocoa butter is widely used as an ointment base (an emollient) and an ingredient in cosmetics.
Cinnamon	Long used to treat GI disorders. It increases intestinal movement, perspiration, and heart rate. In the correct dosage, it's believed to improve circulation. The astringent tannins treat diarrhea; the catechins treat nausea. The essential oils are considered analgesic, antifungal and germicidal.

HERB/PLANT	MEDICINAL USES
Dandelion (Leotodon utumnales, Taraxacum officinale)	Rich in potassium and beta-carotene. It can have a strong diuretic and detoxifying effect and also help the gallbladder and liver remove waste from the body. Chinese herbalists use it for many ailments, including mastitis, tonsillitis, ulcers, colds, and boils.
Dong quai, Chinese Angelica (Angelica sinensis)	It is used in Eastern medicine widely to treat gynecological problems (irregular or delayed menstruation, menopausal hot flashes, pre-menstrual pains and cramps, and utcrine bleeding). Its coumarin derivatives act as antispasmodics that dilate blood vessels. It is also used as a blood purifier and in the treatment of hypertension, ulcers,and rheumatism. Do not take while pregnant; it may stimulate uterine contractions.
Echinacea, Coneflower, Rudbeckia (Echinacea angustlfolia, E. purpurea)	Echinacea is effective against an overabundance of ailments, including colds and flus, yeast infections, herpes sores, and inflammatory diseases. It's a proven antiviral agent and wound-healer, and is considered a nonspecific immune system stimulant.

HERB/PLANT	MEDICINAL USES
Eucalyptus, Blue Gum Tree (Eucalyptus globulus)	The oil from the leaves contains eucalyptol, a powerful antiseptic. Studies show that eucalyptol can kill some influenza viruses. It's approved by the FDA as a cold and flu remedy. It also can kill some kinds of bacteria, making it a good treatment for bronchitis. It also loosens phlegm in the chest, making it a popular ingredient in many lozenges.
Fennel (Foeniculum vulgare)	It can reduce bloating and act as an antispasmodic. An infusion of the seeds relieves sore throats and coughs and acts as a mild expectorant. The crushed seeds can also be used as an eyewash for conjunctivitis. Plant extracts have been used to treat menstrual problems, promote lactation, and facilitate birth. Researchers have documented the validity of these traditional treatments and have found that an extract of the seeds has had an estrogenic effect on lab rats.
Flax (Linum usitatissimum)	Regular consumption can protect against certain types of tumors and may reduce the risk of colon cancer. Some studies have shown it to improve kidney function, lower LDL cholesterol levels, and increase bowel movements.

HERB/PLANT	MEDICINAL USES
Garlic (Allium sativum)	It can reduce cholesterol, blood pressure, and the likelihood of internal blood clots. Other studies show that dietary garlic,as well as other allium vegetables like onions, may prevent stomach cancer. It has been shown to strengthen the immune system in people with HIV/AIDS.
Ginger (Zingiber Officinale)	It is mostly used to treat nausea, indigestion, flu, colds, and arthritis. It is a good all-around tonic.
Ginkgo Biloba, Kew Tree, Maidenhair Tree (Ginkgo Biloba)	Extract of the leaf increases memory performance and learning capacity, deactivates toxic radicals, and improves blood flow. Clinical trials have also shown ginkgo to improve airway passages of asthmatics and to help relieve symptoms of vertigo and tinnitus. High blood pressure and arteriosclerosis can be helped by a concentrated standardized extract.
Ginseng (Panax ginseng, P. trifolium)	Its primary constituents are ginsenosides, which stimulate the cardiovascular and central nervous systems to enhance mental and physical performance. Its Panaxans lower blood sugar and polysaccharides strengthen the immune system and help treat diabetes. Also thought to have antioxidant, anti-aging, and appetite-stimulating properties.

HERB/PLANT	MEDICINAL USES
Goldenseal, Indian dye (Hydrastis Canadensis)	Its alkaloid berberine has been shown to be an antibiotic, antifungal, and antibacterial; it is also considered an immunostimulant. Another alkaloid hydrastine is also considered a potential gastric anti-inflammatory.
Guarana (Paullinia cupana)	It has a high amount of caffeine, which in conjunction with the alkaloids theobromine and theophylline, gives guarana diuretic and stimulant properties. It is used to treat fatigue, headache, migraine, and mild depression, but should not be used long-term. Potential negative side effects include decreased fertility and cardiovascular disease.
Hops (Strobile)	Many of hop's constituents have a sedative effect. It can be used to treat insomnia, anxiety, and restlessness. Its bitter principles are gastrointestinal stimulants and used to treat loss of appetite and indigestion. The bitter acids also have antimicrobial and antibacterial properties. It is also believed to contain chemicals that promote menstruation and show chemo-preventive activity against ovarian and breast cancer.
Kava (Piper methysticum)	In the Pacific Islands, kava is used extensively in ceremonies, festivals, and as a sign of good will. Because

HERB/PLANT	MEDICINAL USES
Kava (Piper methysticum) contd	it numbs any surface it comes into contact with, doctors have used the cut rhizome as a local anesthetic. It contains pain-relieving chemicals that are as strong as aspirin. Kava's main use is as a sedative and treatment for nervous anxiety, restlessness, and stress. It is very effective for treating menstrual cramps. Although it has a sedative effect, users report it clears their mind while relaxing their body.
Kelp (Laminaria digitata, L. versiculosus)	High in iodine, physicians first treated neck goiters with this plant. Since iodine speeds up metabolism, kelp also gained a reputation for treating obesity. Studies show that kelp may also help keep cholesterol and blood pressure low, though care must be taken because its sodium can also increase blood pressure in those who are sensitive to salt.
Lavender (Lavandula angustifolia)	Lavender has had a variety of uses throughout history. Pilgrims used its seeds to expel worms. One recent study has compared the smell of its oil to taking tranquilizers and also found it to work well against insomnia. Another says it may lower blood sugar. Germany's Commission E has approved it as an anti-flatulent and mild stomach disorder treatment.

HERB/PLANT	MEDICINAL USES
Pineapple (Ananas comosus)	Rich in Vitamin C, pineapple contains Bromelain, a protein-splitting enzyme shown to increase bleeding time and reduce aggregation of platelets. Bromelain also has proved effective in killing parasites such as worms.
Rose, Rose Hips, Dog Rose (Rosa Canina)	One of the best sources of Vitamin C, rose oil acts as an astringent and treats inflammation of the mouth. When mixed with other treatments, rose hips are used for flus, colds, and disorders of the urinary tract. They also contain Vitamins A, K, and many B vitamins. The Chinese have used roses, both petals and fruit, for uterine and intestinal disorders.
Saw Palmetto (Serenoa Repens, Serrulata, S. Serrulata)	Chiefly employed to manage prostatic enlargement or benign prostatic hyperplasia (BPH). Saw palmetto relieves flow measures and urinary symptoms associated with an enlarged prostate; it doesn't reduce the enlargement itself. Preparations of saw palmetto have been shown to be effective for treating symptoms of BPH in 18 human clinical trials, several of them indicating much safer effects than the leading pharmaceutical drug.

HERB/PLANT	MEDICINAL USES
Shiitake and Reishi Mushrooms (Lentinula edodes, and Ganoderma lucidum)	A polysaccharide compound in shiitake mushrooms possesses immunostimulant and tumor-preventing properties; it can also prevent platelet adhesion, which causes the clots responsible for coronary artery disease and strokes. Reishi mushrooms may combat tumors, stimulate the immune system, and inhibit the body's production of cholesterol.
Soy, Soybean, Soya (Glycine Max)	Its primary components, isoflavones, bind at estrogen receptor sites. These phytoestrogens (or plant estrogens) are used to treat menopausal symptoms such as hot flashes, and they help to prevent osteoporosis. It has also been used to inhibit hormone dependent (especially estrogen dependent) cancers such as ovarian, breast, and prostate malignancies. Products containing 6.25 grams of soy protein per serving are approved by the FDA to help prevent heart disease and lower cholesterol levels. Soybeans are high in nutritional value and rich in protein, minerals and fiber. They can treat intestinal problems, such as constipation and bowel disease, because of its high cellulose content.

HERB/PLANT	MEDICINAL USES
St. John's Wort, Klamath weed (Hypericum perforatum)	Employed as a healing aid for more than two centuries, it has been shown to be effective as an anti-depressant in mild to moderate depression. It was used by crusaders and Civil War soldiers to treat battle wounds. Native Americans used it for many uses: pre-menstrual syndrome (PMS), fevers, diarrhea, rheumatism, snakebite, and skin disorders.
Tea, Green Tea, Black Tea (Camellia sinensis, Thea sinensis)	Green tea has been shown to have a wide variety of medicinal effects. It has antibacterial properties, including the bacteria that cause dental decay, and it has been shown to lower certain types of cholesterol. Both types of tea contain a large number of strong antioxidants. It can also help with digestive tract problems ranging from diarrhea to cancer.
Valerian, Setwell, Phu, All-heal (Valeriana officinalis)	It is primarily used as an aid for sleep problems, nervousness, anxiety, and headaches.
White Willow, European Willow (Salix Alba)	It was widely used throughout history for fevers and joint pain. It has also been recognized as a diuretic, an eye disease treatment, and an aid in childbirth. In 1850, a derivative was synthesized as an active ingredient in aspirin, one of the world's most popular medications. It has recently been accepted as a prophylactic that reduces the probability of heart disease and stroke by affecting clotting and stimulating inflammation of the blood.

HERB/PLANT	MEDICINAL USES
Witch Hazel (Hamamelis Virginiana)	Witch hazel is a rich source of tannins, which tighten skin proteins to provide improved increased resistance to inflammation, assist the healing of broken skin, and help repair damaged blood vessels. It's useful for a variety of skin conditions: varicose veins, bruises, cysts, hemorrhoids, or tumors. When taken in oral form, it can help with excessive bleeding during menstruation and is an effective preventative when taken before surgery. Native American tribes used witch hazel extensively for treating more than 30 ailments that include the following: colds, tumors, skin problems, bloody dysentery, tuberculosis, sore eyes, arthritis, hemorrhage after childbirth, and heart problems.
Wormwood, Artemisia (Artemisia absinthum)	Native American tribes use this as a vermifuge (anti-parasitic stunning agent), as well as for treating strained muscles, head and chest colds, broken limbs, tuberculosis, stomach ailments, and venereal diseases. It contains some bitter constituents that stimulate the secretion of digestive fluids. It improves absorption of nutrients, strengthens the digestive system, and can ease gas and bloating.

HERB/PLANT	MEDICINAL USES
Yarrow (also called Milfoil, Nosebleed, Woundwort, Stanchweed) Achillea millefolium	It has been shown to arrest internal and external bleeding. It also can relieve gastrointestinal ailments, reduce fevers, stimulate appetite, and treat thrombosis. Yarrow's essential volatile oil contains chamazulene, which acts as an anti-inflammatory, an antiallergenic, and an antispasmodic.

Seasonal Tip:

Use sterling silver flatware to benefit from its antiseptic properties.

Climate Influence and Grain Consumption

Our climate influences our daily requirements and consumption of nutrients. Grains by volume of daily food consumption based on climate and temperature vary from 20% during the winter to 10% during the summer.

Our Bodies Process Foods According To Seasonal States

How we process food is different throughout the seasons. In the summer, our cells are expanded; thus, summer solstice marks our fullest state of expansion, allowing nutrition and foods to flow quickly through us. In the autumn, our cells move towards a contracted state, which is marked by winter solstice as the peak of our contraction. As the autumn process begins, our body and cells naturally contract to hold in all the nutritional value we need to manage the seasonal change in available foods.

The idea that we can get everything we need because of imported food is only partially true because we are still being exposed to the elements of our own seasons. It may be a balance depending on your needs. In the winter, our cells contract as they retain energy and substance. In the spring, they begin to loosen and release as they awaken to the desire to cleanse. Our cell density adjusts with seasons. This is why it is so important to consume seasonal foods of like density. Think of putting a hard object into a delicate net; it will rip and damage it. It is the same as with our summer body density. We are meant to eat watermelons, salads, and water-filled foods, not roots, beans, and hard nuts that require stronger tissues to break down and digest them.

The quality of what we eat and what we put on our skin affects our health and well-being. The less processed or refined foods we consume, the better. Not only is this a matter of digestion and nutrients, but it is also a matter of keeping unknown ingredients out of our system. This is also true when we consider what we put on our skin. The further we get away from the ingredients provided to us by nature, the less positive the effects will be. The closer we are to natural formulas that complement the season we are in, the stronger and more satisfying is the effect. We should avoid at all cost chemically engineered foods, as well as creams and cosmetics for our skin that use separated elements from their original states. It is deeply rooted in our society to use these types of products, but the effects on our body from an inward and outward perspective should be noted.

Our Food Attractions Match the Seasons

Just as our bodies process foods according to the seasons, our attractions to foods are also guided by the seasons. These attractions are usually based on the seasonal ease of digestibility. In the winter, it is perfectly natural not to be interested in most salads, choosing instead more seasonal soups or stews. We are attracted to foods whose density matches ours as it changes through the year. In summertime, we eat high water, lower-density, expanded foods. In

winter, we eat foods that are more compressed and dense, matching our own cellular makeup. In autumn, we eat foods that are high in vitamin and mineral contents as our bodies prepare for the scarcity of nutrients in the winter and look for nutrition to be stored. In spring, we eat foods that are fresh and growing, sprouting from the ground, clean and cleansing. The foods we eat affect how we act, feel, and think. This includes our moods and how we handle stress in our environment. Our bodies naturally release toxins and cleanse on a regular basis in our normal bodily functions. As we are cleansed, our minds become clear and our natural good judgment returns. This process of intake and rejection should be kept in balance—never put more in if the previous meal has not left.

Another way to eat seasonally is to shop for seasonal foods at your local farmers' market. This benefits us in many ways. It supports the local economy, community, and sustainable farming, and it allows you to find many seasonal foods you'd never find in a grocery store. The fruits and vegetables are at their peak of freshness and tastiness. Eating these vegetables, fruits, and nuts helps our bodies, skin, and other organs adapt to the local environment as well. When they're allowed to ripen in the field, then brought straight to you, there is no long-distance shipping. It's easier to reconnect with the seasons, the earth, and the cycles of nature. The farmers and vendors are always ready to help you with seasonal cooking suggestions, meal tips, and recipes. I always learn something new at the farmers' market!

Seasonal Food Preparations

❖ **Spring–** Begin the process of detoxing from energy that was stored throughout the winter. Our cells begin to open up and expand just a bit to allow the flow through them. Begin to eat some small spring, early-sprouted greens, like leeks, scallions, and young onions, which are high in digestive enzymes. This is the time of year to drink the most water, supplemented with milk thistle as an aid for detox. Eat well-cooked grains, which help to shed the lining of our intestinal tract and prepare us for a light, raw-food, vitamin-rich diet. This is a good time to consider a colonic for our system to help the liver, skin, and kidneys with processing the release of waste. The best colonic preparations make use of ocean water. This will eliminate any skin conditions caused by the release of toxins accumulated during winter months.

If we ate only raw fruits and vegetables, our bodies wouldn't have to make digestive enzymes. They already contain all the digestive enzymes necessary for their digestion. The more processed the food, the more digestive enzymes we have to make to extract the nutrients that the food has to offer.

❖ **Summer**– Summer is the time of fruits, salads, and seafood. Combine these with your daily intake of vitamins and minerals, and add silica for skin, nails and hair to compensate for the times spent outdoors in the sun, water, and other elements.

Summer is also a good time to add an amino acid called taurine to our diet. It builds strength in our muscle fibers to help prevent injuries during summer sports. During summer, our nutrients flow through us without depositing or storing. Watch your energy level to see if you need more Vitamin C and B to sustain your long, fun days.

❖ **Autumn**– Autumn is the most intriguing and important season in our year as this is the time of accumulating, repairing, and restoring our systems. We go into a cycle of storage mode, transitioning with rich, nutrient-abundant vegetables and late summer fruits to supply us nutrients during the resource-scarce winter months. We will need to add Vitamins A and E, taken gradually, as they are oils and not water-soluble. Spread them over autumn and winter on a daily basis. Start taking DLPA supplement midway through the autumn to ensure your mood factor will remain constant: this will hold your endorphin levels up on the days when you cannot exercise outdoors any longer. Physical activities are important as they produce desirable hormones and endorphins. Think of exercise as your vitamin for the day. By the end of the autumn, add more protein to your daily meals. Add L-Tyrosine to your DLPA and continue taking it until the second week of spring.

❖ **Winter–** In the winter, our body is programmed to use more stored nutrients and stored energy. Our cells are at their densest state, which is why our meals should be small, rich, and cooked or pickled. In an effort to continue to maintain nutrient levels, it is helpful to reach for compotes, stews, soups, and savory foods for beautiful, glowing skin when fresh greens are limited. Due to the lack of sun, it is important to get some exercise and keep the brain stimulated with indoor social activities and games.

When people get in bad moods all the time, they should reach for bananas and fish. They will help restore serotonin connection. Taking a 5-HTP supplement will be an additional help.

For a list of Seasonal Fruit and Vegetable Availability (by Hemisphere), see Appendix B.

Just as we eat differently at different times of the year, so too do we consume differently during different times of the day. This may be obvious, but what most people do not correlate is the relationship between body functions, light and dark (day and night), and available seasonal foods and their preparation. It is a fallacy that breakfast is the most important meal of the day. I have found this to be untrue because eating food while the body is in a cycle of elimination is completely counter-intuitive to our body functions. If I wait longer to start eating and follow the natural cycle that calls for drinking water during morning hours, I help my body eliminate toxins with greater success and ease. I find that my mind works better, I have far more energy, and I'm in tune with my natural cycle. This, in turn, gives me energy on-demand throughout the day. No yogi or monk eats before noon.

226

CHAPTER TEN

SUPPLEMENTS

The importance of supplementing cannot be stressed enough. Our foods no longer hold the saturation of vitamins and minerals to sufficiently deliver needed nutrition. Supplementing is a key to our ageless living. This is where the seasons come into play by dictating the supplements we need to take into consideration.

People are amazed by my ability to heal. Cuts and scrapes heal in 24 hours or less because I maintain a high nutritional level from the foods I eat, the vitamins I take, and supplements I use.

Seasonal Supplement Suggestions

Winter

- ❖ Calcium and Potassium Citrate

- ❖ Biotin and Folic Acid

- ❖ Vita Sprouts cap (B complex, Maximum Life brand)

- ❖ Vitamin E (400 mg)

- Vitamin A (50,000 IU) with pectin

- Meta C with biologically active metabolites (buffered, 4,000 mg)

- Parsley extract (supports adrenal glands)

- Lecithin

- D3

- 5-HT- as needed

Spring

- Meta C with biologically active metabolites (buffered, 4,000 mg)

- Taurine (1,000 mg)

- CQ10 (100 mg)

- Probiotics

- Raspberry whole leaf extract (drops)

- Milk Thistle

- Silica

Summer

- Meta C with biologically active metabolites (buffered) (4,000 mg)

- Taurine (1,000 mg)

- CQ10 (100 mg)

- Biotin (3,000 mcg)

❖ Folic Acid (800 mcg)

❖ Calcium with Magnesium

❖ Zinc

Autumn

❖ Meta C with biologically active metabolites (buffered) (4,000 mg)

❖ Vita Sprouts cap (B complex)

❖ DHEA

❖ Calcium from Coral

❖ Plain Bromelain (450 mg)

❖ Vitamin A 50,000 IU

❖ Folic Acid (800 mcg)

❖ Lecithin

❖ D3

❖ Folic Acid

Second Half of Autumn, add

❖ Vitamin E (400 mg)

❖ Vitamin A (25,000 IU) with pectin

❖ Parsley extract (supports adrenal glands)

As previously mentioned, we are well aware of the winter blues called Seasonal Affective Disorder (or SAD). There are natural-light electric bulbs available to supplement the necessary light; however, it does not produce enough D vitamins for all of our body functions. Winter is the time to consider taking Vitamin D3 to help us compensate. Another important supplement is L Tyrosine in combination with Lecithin, because it helps the brain's cognitive skills.

Benefits of Supplements

Vitamin A

I find that Vitamin A and its antioxidant effect boost the immune system. It also protects the body from pollutants, aging, and cancer according to the National Cancer Institute. I take a double dose of Vitamin A in the winter. Vitamin A is responsible for healthier-looking skin and prevents wrinkles. Vitamin A can improve the quality of your hair, eyes, teeth, and gums.

Butter has high Vitamin A content and is readily absorbed into our system. Just as butter lubricates a pan, it acts as a moisturizer for your intestine. When you heat up other oils in a pan, they thicken and create a heavy residue, which is also how they act internally. You will need steel wool or an abrasive scouring pad to remove it. Try melting different types of oils in a pan and that will tell you how they act inside you. I use only oils that do not stick and run off the pan easily.

Vitamin B

I find that Vitamin B is most helpful in dealing with stress. It should be taken at noon with food as it may interfere with sleep if taken in the evening. Our lives are moving faster and faster; we become involved in many things without the time to rest in between them. As exciting as it sounds, it does create stress for our body to keep up with our desires to be involved in so many activities. If we want to enjoy living to the fullest, we need to support our system with B vitamins. They support our nervous system during these high-demand periods.

Vitamin C

I take Vitamin C in buffered form in combination with biologically active metabolites all year round and in high doses to assure that my skin has plenty for the rebuilding of my connective tissue after having it challenged for so long (as I mentioned earlier with regard to my illness). Buffered Vitamin C is our fuel for life. It gives us energy to get through the day, and we need to take enough to continue replacing our cells for a sound structure. Vitamin C is the glue of our cells. Without it, we would have no collagen or elastin, and our skin would deteriorate. Your need for Vitamin C is directly connected to your body's ability to extract Vitamin C from your food and your current need for cellular repair. In other words, if you are running low on energy, you may need more Vitamin C. Since it is water soluble and any excess is easily flushed out, you cannot take too much.

Vitamin D

This supplement is extremely important to your metabolic processes and your mood. If affects your bone density, your hormones, and ability to detox. Synthesized Vitamin D becomes Vitamin D3 through sun exposure. It also affects neuromuscular function and lowers inflammation and cell reproduction. We continue to find more links between Vitamin D and our body's functioning every day.

Vitamin E

Vitamin E is essential for the repair of scar tissue. It can prevent stretch marks and help the body heal from minor scratches and surgical scars. It should not be taken internally before or after surgery because it can cause bleeding (i.e., it is a blood thinner). It can be applied topically afterwards. Use it to ease PMS, prevent miscarriage, reduce hot flashes, and relieve menopause discomfort, or use it for pregnancy and lactation, and when on estrogen or the pill. It also protects bodies from pollutants and aids recovery from migraines. It is required that you take zinc with Vitamin E if you want to maintain the Vitamin E levels in the blood.

If diamonds are a woman's best friend, I say so are Vitamins C, E, and A.

Minerals

The mineral balance of our body is created by their proper ratio. This is where the need for replenishment of the minerals is determined. Only when we supply the minerals needed for metabolic processes will we experience a symptom-free life, which we call optimum health.

It is known that our body can use minerals without the support of vitamins, but it can't utilize vitamins without the support of minerals. We are made of minerals suspended in fluids. Most vitamins are manufactured from within our own body. This is why daily replenishment of minerals through food, mineral-rich waters, mineral-rich cosmetics, sun exposure, and adequate reparative sleep are the foundation to our health and quality of our life.

Trace Minerals

Trace minerals are the co-factors or tools that make everything happen in the body, and they make up the structure of the body from bones to teeth. You need less than 100 mg of trace minerals a day, but you must have them for healthy living. You can trace almost every sickness and ailment to mineral deficiency. Minerals come from the soil, and depleted soil means depleted minerals. Women tend to need more minerals than men, while men need other types of vitamins and proteins more. Our body consists of the same balance of liquid ions and minerals as deep seawater.

In my **Replete**™ seasonal formulas, I bring pristine Hawaiian, 2,000-year-old deep seawater from a depth of 3,000 feet to you so you can access the minerals you need every day. Your vitality will increase, as will your sense of well-being. This gives you confidence for a successful day in business, life, and pleasure after work hours.

The essential macro minerals (i.e., minerals you need more of) are calcium, magnesium, sodium, potassium, and phosphorus.

Calcium

This is one of the most important minerals for women. Not only does it prevent osteoporosis, it reduces stress, migraines, cramps, and water retention. It is essential for regulating the heartbeat, muscle growth and contraction, and transmission of nerve contractions. Calcium deficiency is manifested in leg cramps, nervousness, heart palpitations, brittle nails, aching back or joints, tooth decay, and even numbness in the arms or legs. Calcium can be found in many leafy green vegetables, fish, and sesame seeds, which can be found during different cycles throughout the year. In fact, broccoli and cauliflower have more calcium per ounce than milk.

Calcium taken with magnesium will reduce muscle cramps.

Calcium taken with potassium reduces the effects of caffeine.

Magnesium

Magnesium activates enzymes to metabolize carbohydrates and helps strengthen nerves and muscles.

Sodium

Sodium is extremely important for a healthy life because it aids in the formation of digestive juices and helps maintain water balance throughout the cells. In addition to maintaining adequate blood volume and pressure, it's responsible for muscle tone and function. Salt plays a role in nervous system communication through electrical charge conduct. Ocean (sea) salts are always preferred: they do not cause the bloating that rock salt does. Sea salt is filled with needed nutrients and trace minerals, electrolytes without which we cannot function.

Potassium

Potassium is necessary to maintain fluid and electrolyte balance. It is also needed for heart, nerve, skeletal, and digestive functioning. A lack of potassium may result in fatigue, irritability, muscle cramps, and high blood pressure. It is naturally found in dark leafy greens, sweet potatoes, dried apricots, peaches, prunes, raisins, squash (e.g., acorn, butternut, Hubbard, zucchini, and other winter squash), fish, avocados, mushrooms, and bananas.

Phosphorus

Phosphorus makes up one percent of our total body weight. It is present in every cell; the majority is in our bones and teeth. It plays an important role in our utilization of carbohydrates and fats, as well as the synthesis of protein for the growth, maintenance, and repair of tissue and cells. It is crucial for production of ATP, an energy-storing molecule. Phosphorus supports the contraction of muscles, kidney functioning, nerve conduction, and heartbeat regularity. Phosphorus works in conjunction with B vitamins. Deficiency in phosphorus can lead to anemia, muscle pain, improper bone formation, weakened immune system, and numbness. Some high phosphorus foods are rice, oat bran, pumpkin, squash, sunflower and watermelon seeds, toasted wheat germ, cheese, sesames seeds, nuts, edamame, and flax seeds.

Essential *Micro* Minerals

Zinc, Iron, Copper, Boron, Manganese, Chromium, Germanium, Selenium, and Iodine.

Zinc

Zinc helps regenerate collagen (as does Vitamin C).

Iron

One of the main functions of iron is to carry oxygen to the tissues. It also activates the formation of bone, brain, and muscle tissue. Sometimes, sea vegetables such as Kombu and other seaweeds or kelp can provide five times the iron of meats.

Copper

Cooper is needed by your skin to connect collagen and elastin: it is also used for the formation of melanin, your natural sun protection.

Selenium

An important antioxidant and anti-inflammatory that can help alleviate psoriasis. Deficiency is common in people with metastatic melanoma. Selenium works with Vitamin E for your beautiful healthy skin.

Iodine

Iodine is a trace mineral essential to thyroid regulation.

Essential Fatty Acids

Your body cannot produce these on its own, and they are critical for the maintenance of your cell membranes. The stronger your cell membranes are, the younger you will look and feel. You can get essential fatty acids from flaxseed and fish oils.

Bioflavonoids

They offer a powerful boost to your immune system and help your body react appropriately to viruses, carcinogens, and allergens. They help the body react to damage caused by pollution and your normal metabolizing processes. This reduces wrinkles and signs of aging, along with working to support your internal organs. They can be found in many herbs, vegetables, and fruits, as well as green teas, wine, citrus fruits (especially the pith, the white part between the peel and the fruit itself) like lemons, oranges, and grapefruits. Parsley, grape seeds, and dark chocolate also contain bioflavonoids.

Grape Seed Extract (Resveratrol)

A popular supplement with many benefits, it can prevent blood clots, inhibit the growth of cancer cells, act as an anti-inflammatory, and lower blood sugar levels. Resveratrol is present in red wine, and the health benefits of this have long been known as the "French Paradox."

Amino Acids

Amino acids are a product of protein breakdown from our foods, and then they become building blocks for our cells.

Botanicals

Nature provides us with botanicals. We need botanical extracts that not only preserve, but also support our seasonal needs for nutrients, whether they are herbs from different regions of the world or herbs grown locally.

Silica

A necessary component for hair and nail growth, especially after surgery, cosmetic procedures, childbirth, high stress, or trauma. Great restorative aid after losing hair from harsh chemical hair processing.

Supplement Purchasing Information

When purchasing your supplements, make sure they contain all natural ingredients, avoiding the cheaper synthetic ones. After all, our DNA is built on a crystal formation, and it needs the replacement of the like. Buy from a reputable source that can answer any questions you have.

Overlooked (but necessary) Supplements

Water

Sweetwater in the morning is essential to the following:

- ❖ Activating elimination
- ❖ Detoxification
- ❖ Hydradration of the cells and system
- ❖ Removing water soluble toxins
- ❖ Assisting in washing through the cells

Ocean water at night before bedtime is essential to do the following:

- ❖ Replenish lost minerals and trace minerals
- ❖ Restore healthy functioning of our intestinal tract
- ❖ Initiate weight loss
- ❖ Provide many other components needed for nightly repairs

CHAPTER TEN - SUPPLEMENTS

Sunlight

A moderate amount of sunshine each day is known to provide us with Vitamin D: however, it also has many of the following benefits that are overlooked and still not understood by us:

- ❖ Analgesic (pain-killing) properties

- ❖ Fat burning (lack of Vitamin D can lead to obesity)

- ❖ Improves evening alertness

- ❖ It's a natural antiseptic (i.e., can kill viruses, bacteria, molds, fungi, and mites on skin and other surfaces)

- ❖ Boosts mood, metabolism, and immune system

- ❖ Better sleep

- ❖ Helps balance hormones

Try to avoid prolonged sunlight between the hours of 10 a.m. and 4 p.m. during summer months.

For now, we have to concern ourselves with our nutritional needs. At some point in our human existence, there is the possibility through evolution where we may find ourselves no longer concerned with nutritional content of grown food because we will have adapted to drawing energy from other sources and be able to convert it for needed nutrients within our own system. By thinking this, we may begin to consider where we will next draw our energy from in order to adapt to our changing environment. Some think it might be air, and others say it might be possible for sunlight or water to be our source of our energy to come. We know we cannot live without air, sunlight, and water.

We are at the point where substituting and supplementing is essential. Just think how inconceivable the ideas of a cell phone or computer were to someone 200 years ago. Yet, we cannot imagine living without them today. Do not discard the possibility that one day our bodies will acquire the nutrients they need through different means as part of progressive evolution.

The Mayan Periodic Chart of the Elements

Dr. Olree has traced all of the elements to their participatory function in the life process. His theory stipulates that each of the 64 codons (—the basic units of the genetic code—) requires its own unique mineral, and thus, greatly expands our list of vital nutrients.

I chose the Mayan periodic chart to show you the simplicity of the proportion of elements with which our body ideally functions. This is the best existing guide for knowing how to bring our body to balance through selecting needed elements when choosing our food or anything else with which we come in contact.

The Mayan Periodic Chart of the Elements

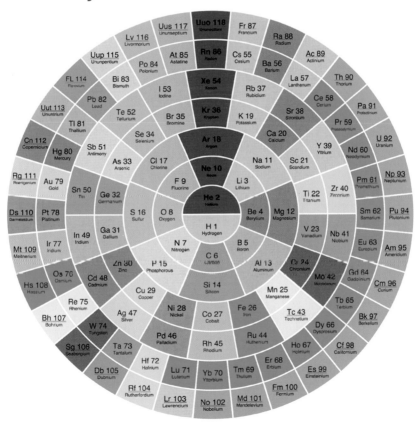

MayanPeriodic.com

The Mayan Periodic Table of Elements, named for its similarity to the ancient Mesoamerica calendar, is based on electron shells. The shells are shown as concentric circles. Each row in the tabular form is shown as a ring.

This arrangement shows some aspects of the elements better than the traditional table. But first, some background.

In some schools, all the boys want to be the captain of the football team, and all the girls want to be a cheerleader. It's good to have goals. In the world of chemistry, all the atoms want to be noble gas. Noble gases have their outer electron shell completely filled. They are content. For example, Argon (Ar) has its outer shell filled.

Chlorine, on the other hand, needs one more electron to fill its outer shell. Chlorine (Cl) is so close to completing its outer shell, it can taste it. Where can it get the extra electron? Interestingly, Sodium (Na) has the opposite problem. Its outer shell has one extra electron. If they combine, both of them achieve their dream of having a filled outer shell.

The noble gases are in the vertical column above the center of the chart. The elements to the right of a noble gas have one extra electron; the elements directly on the left need one electron to fill their outer shell.

Okay, what does this chart show better than the traditional table?

1. The reactivity of the elements. The elements closest to the noble gases are so close to becoming a noble gas they can feel it. This makes them more eager and more reactive, since all they need is to gain or lose one electron. As you move away from the noble gases along the concentric circles, the elements get less and less reactive. Since they are so far from being a noble gas, they don't really think it is worth the effort.

2. The proportions of compounds. The proportion of elements can be guessed by looking at the *hops* that an element must take to get to the noble gases. The guideline is that for elements to combine, one should be from the left and one from the right. The number of hops an atom takes to get to the vertical line must equal the number its partner on the other side takes, since one is gaining an electron and one is losing one.

For example, sodium has one hop to the left to get to the vertical line and chlorine one to the right. This implies they combine in a one-to-one ratio.

Aluminum needs three hops left to get vertical, and oxygen needs just two.

Since the number of hops needs to be the same on both sides, we need two Aluminum atoms to make the journey and three Oxygen atoms to make it equal. This implies Al(2)O(3) is a good possibility for a compound.

This guideline only works for elements fairly near the noble gases. This chart is only a rough guide since the inner shells of elements are not always filled before the outer shells.

3. Transition elements. The transition elements area usually shown as a block of elements apart from the others. The Mayan arrangement shows them to be integrated with the others.

4. The behavior of the elements is representative of the human behavior and the needs of our skin.

5. Our skin and body travel through the chart of elements as the seasons change to connect with what is needed.

6. Spring and summer are male energy seasons. With their corresponding elements, they have more outer electron lines for connecting. Autumn and winter represent female energy elements with inner hops that are looking to be filled.

7. The left side of the chart represents heavier elements and the right side lighter ones that are closest to light and exist in greater numbers to balance the chart on the left.

8. Taking supplements is essential; minerals, vitamins, and herbs, as well as eating natural foods on an as needed basis can improve your quality and enjoyment of life. Here are a few examples why. Iodine, the densest mineral that our body uses, is necessary for reproduction of life. If the thyroid gland is deficient of Iodine then infertility sets in. Phosphorous gives the cells energy for all protein activities. Carbon is the center of our lives; it is the halfway point of the top quark and the heaviest mineral. Life is impossible without carbon. Boron is a subatomic stabilizer: it keeps our energy balanced. Calcium and magnesium are the center of the light energy to three-dimensional life conversion in the form of chlorophyll. Our sodium and potassium balance represents our cliff between life and death, too little or too much and life is cut short. Now, we get to the role of quark. That is our sub-atomic particle alphanon, a zero value with no polarity; it's the lightest noble gas in our body.

9. All these aspects need to be considered when preparing food and choosing anything that we come in contact with or connect with.

CHAPTER ELEVEN

WATER: THE ELIXIR OF LIFE

Water is one of the key elements of healthy skin. Not only can dehydration have severe effects on your skin, but also on your overall health and sense of well-being. Skin needs water for proper function, and the amount of water in our skin changes seasonally. If pores become clogged or blocked with oils, dead cells, and dirt, the skin cannot breathe or pull water and air from the atmosphere. The least water is retained in the skin cells during the winter, making our skin prone to becoming dry and chapped when exposed to the elements. The opposite is true during the summer when we hold the most water in the skin cells, making our skin more resilient during our times spent outdoors.

Our Cell Membranes

Our cells are approximately 65-90% water, or they should be optimally when they are contained by a healthy cell membrane. The water content of our cells determines how supple and smooth our skin is, along with how youthful looking. Water gives our cells shape outside of the framework of our cellular structure. How they are organized is based on our DNA. Our cells will either age or they will self-destruct when damage cannot easily be repaired. Our skin is about 70% water. Keeping it well hydrated is a two-part process. The first part includes drinking the water we need, and the second part entails using seasonal creams that are natural and allow the skin to be protected while it breathes. Smooth, ageless skin is a factor of getting the water we need, natural oils, minerals, and a healthy pH balance during our seasonal care. Most minerals we use are water-soluble, so it is not healthy to drink excessive amounts of water as the minerals are washed away. Do not force yourself to drink water when you are not thirsty, but do drink a glass daily when you awaken. Your body has the ability to naturally ask for it. Be aware of the signs.

Signs You Need Water:

- ❖ Persistent Fatigue
- ❖ Lethargy
- ❖ Muscle Weakness
- ❖ Cramps
- ❖ Headaches
- ❖ Dizziness
- ❖ Nausea
- ❖ Forgetfulness

❖ Confusion

❖ Rapid Breathing

❖ Increased Heart Rate

❖ Thirst

❖ Total Absence of Thirst (in extreme conditions)

Water flushes out the kidneys, which process about 200 quarts of our blood each day to rid our bodies of 2% of waste and extra water. When our bodies have taken what they need from our food and have used the energy it provides, the remainder is sent to the blood. The kidneys cleanse it further, because a build-up of waste in the bloodstream will damage our bodies. Water reaches the entire system efficiently, skipping digestive processes and making it the best vehicle to deliver necessary minerals. Conversely, distilled water will bind with and remove minerals as it moves throughout the system.

Note: People with serious illness should get professional advice when starting to change their diets so they understand the right balance of foods, vitamins, and botanicals that suit their individual needs. Even two people with the same illness need adjustments specific to their individual bodies. Always implement gradual change.

When taking medication for a prolonged period of time, it

is common to develop "side effects." In fact, most of them are mineral or vitamin deficiency symptoms. All pharmaceuticals rely on assistance from the body's resources for processing. Refer to the pamphlet or list provided with your medication to see what may be the culprit in your case.

The Fountain of Youth

"The Fountain of Youth" has been a mythological reference for as long as can be remembered. It has been illustrated as something you become immersed in, which then makes your skin look young, and you become vital all over again. Your fountain of youth is specific to you, and it is directly related to what you consume and your ability to retain it, keeping you physically and mentally young and looking attractive.

When we are formed in our mothers' wombs, we are immersed in water; when we die, we evaporate.

We are dependent on continuous replenishment of the vital building blocks for our systems. After all, only when we do not have the needed components, the next generation of cells will be compromised. We call this aging.

It is best to go to the source: *WATER*.

Detail of Fontana Della Giovinezza

This original Fountain of Youth fresco "Fontana Della Giovinezza" (circa 1420), is located at the Castello Della Manta, Italy. This is what we are striving for and can come closer to when we live in rhythm with the seasons.

Some people think that the fountain of youth attributed to Ponce de Leon's expedition to St. Augustine, Florida. It is the oldest city in the U.S.

Nutrients in Water

We are only as young as the minerals we hold. We only get old when our minerals are depleted. Our bodies continuously repair and replace our damaged or dying cells. When we have all the essential minerals we need, the damage of time is minimized, and we are then able to process all our nutrients and supplements. As long as we have all the necessary building blocks starting with minerals, we can continue to replace our cells, and diseases of the gastrointestinal tract can be healed. We can have virtually ageless cells!

Replete Aqua™

Due to overfarming, which causes mineral-depleted soil and therefore poor food quality, I supplement with ionic minerals from deep ocean water that are easily absorbed. These are drawn from the ocean depths off the Hawaiian coast, over 3,000 feet beneath the ocean surface. At this depth, this pure water is 2,000 years old. This naturally pristine ocean water is pathogen, chemical, and pollution-free with over 20 times the mineral content of surface ocean water. **Replete Aqua™** is superior because of its close match to a human cell. **Replete Aqua™** contains 90+ trace minerals and has the highest blend of magnesium and calcium for healthy bones, teeth, blood, heart, digestion, increased fat burn, and improved nerve transmission.

The following chart lists the amounts of some of the minerals in **Replete Aqua™**.

MINERAL CONTENT IN REPLETE AQUA™ (ppm)		
	Replete™	**Raw**
TDS	55077	42509
Source of TDS	NAT	NAT
Hardness	8048	6985.6
pH	7.8	7.4
Bicarbonates	177	154
Calcium	520	454
Copper	0.37	0.01
Iron	1.24	0.01
Magnesium	1700	1474
Manganese	0.24	0.04
Phosphorous	0	0.28
Potassium	960	554
Silica	370	240.5
Sodium	14000	11796
Zinc	1.24	0.01

(For a complete list, including trace minerals, see Appendix C)

Why Ocean Water Is Different

Deep ocean water is the perfect source for our renewal processes. With seasonal living, we have discovered that deep ocean water supports life; thus, it supports cell growth. When Dr. Robert Ballard discovered the source of ionic trace minerals, it opened new doors and thinking around the type of water and cells required to create and sustain life, as well as create living cells. He discovered that only six miles below the ocean's surface, everywhere those ionic trace minerals were present, the areas were teeming with life. Even without sunlight, the ecosystem was living on the broken down trace minerals and were prolifically reproducing.

Trace Minerals

Living cells use trace minerals to develop and keep our DNA alive and ageless. It makes sense to keep adding trace minerals to our diet as a supplement. Many years ago, we were able to get most of the minerals we needed from the foods we were eating, but now mineral-depleted soils offer mineral-depleted crops. Adding these trace minerals to our diet or skin care regimen is a sure way of getting them back into our system.

In the sea surrounding the Hawaiian Islands, the water is

balanced to the same pH as the human body. The unique pH of water in this area is due to hydrothermal vents around the islands. These are mineral-rich areas created by tectonic plates moving apart below the ocean's surface, and the warmth created there. Chemosynthetic Archaea form the base of the food chain, supporting diverse organisms that thrive in this environment and creating a powerful cycle of life.

Whales come here instinctively to give birth; the mineral and pH balance of the water is the same pH the baby whales are developed in. Areas where whales go for birthing are also high in trace minerals.

There are many types of minerals found in the natural state of our systems, but the content of ocean water best matches the environment in which we were created. The two are almost identical. Natural sea salt and now ocean water can provide many minerals not available from other food or liquid sources. When I realized that by drinking a small amount of ocean water, I was reestablishing my natural mineral balance, adjusting my body's pH, and enabling my system to do its repair work, my curiosity was born. I became very interested in other uses for this water. This ocean water is the ultimate resource; it provides the building blocks for our repair with minerals and salts, as well as plays a key role in the world's water cycle. The deep ocean water in my **Replete**™ formulas allow the skin to easily absorb a unique balance of trace minerals we could not obtain in smaller molecules elsewhere.

To really understand the spirit of life, be an observer of your own life and those around you. Notice that when you take your dog to the beach and the dog drinks the seawater, it is not science telling the dog to drink the seawater. Shetland ponies live entirely on seaweed and seawater during winter months, it is their natural intelligence and instinct to do so. When babies are developing in the womb, they breathe, exhale, and drink amniotic fluid, which is in the baby's lungs when they are born. This is the spirit of life's handiwork in action and speaks more to the type of intelligence we should be noticing. If you are still not convinced that seawater is natural to us, then taste your teardrop or your sweat! This is what we need to replace, our natural fluids rich with amino acids and trace elements. It is all that is needed by our system for us to thrive.

With seasonal living, you are taught to pay attention to the seasons and the natural methods and language our body communicates with. We have noticed the body's response to natural ocean water and embraced it as a key ingredient in topical skin applications and in supplements.

Minerals, in particular, must work together and not be in excess of one or another. It is best to reach for naturally created formulas without too much alteration within their balance.

Seasonal Tip:

I especially enjoy my **Replete Rejuvenating Mist™** while traveling, followed with my natural botanical skin care serums. I personally add trace minerals to my food, and I take 2 oz. of ionic trace minerals by drinking my **Replete Aqua™** every night before going to bed, which has a positive influence on my skin and energy.

Photo by Joshua Horowitz

CHAPTER TWELVE

EMBRACING CHANGE

The way to success lies in apprehending and giving actuality to the way of the universe, which, as a law running through end and beginning, brings about all phenomena in time. Thus, each step attained forthwith becomes a preparation for the next. Time is no longer a hindrance, but the means of making actual what is potential. — *Tao*

Change has five stages. The first is Creative, which links to Intention, which then activates the following stages:

Four Cardinal Virtues in Humanity

❖ Sublime → links to love →embraces all other attributes

❖ Success → links to morals → regulates and organizes expressions

❖ Furthering → links to justice → creates the conditions to receive

❖ Perseverance→links to wisdom→brings enduring conditions

Change is solely based on the principles of polarity with positive and negative charges.

Intelligent Choices

You cannot fear what you do not use... there is no need to be fearful of the natural world because there is usually an antidote.

Creating new habits around the way we live, love, participate in, or experience our lives is a multifaceted prospect. Fortunately, every aspect has many areas that compound the positives of making those choices every step of the way. Courage is needed, and then the choice must be made, and once it is, you are on your way to implementing positive changes in your life. At face value, it may look strange and unfamiliar. It is best not to act in haste and reject the possibility of something new when it presents itself. A shift will occur, and you will begin to notice that people will have a different response to you; your behavior and attitude will assume a new position, and you will learn and experience a more harmonious life.

Happiness is a Choice—Choose It

Change is not difficult. It is our resistance to change that creates the difficulty. When you finally come to the point of recognizing that you need to make changes, this realization could have come about in many ways and at many levels for anyone. For some people, it takes the most extreme amount of pressure. They may have to lose their families, their jobs, their money, or worst of all, their health. Often, it is only at this extreme moment that they begin to accept the fact they need to make a shift. Only when they have finally been diagnosed with cancer or some other life-threatening ailment, or have hit emotional and financial rock bottom, are they forced to see the light. You do not need to wait that long. You can take a moment to recognize what you already know intuitively and begin to address those issues right now.

There are several ways of looking at this in clear, simplified terms:

Willingness to Change for the better =

Optimal Living = Optimal Health

Courage Comes From Willpower Rooted In Faith

Photo by Drew Altizer

With the two together, you can accomplish anything and become all that is within reach of your potential for an exceptional life. I have found that what helps me most to change behaviors and habits is focusing on the benefits that will arise from the change. For example, I know that after I work out, I feel energized. I love how it creates a positive attitude towards my work, my surroundings, and sense of well-being. I have the stamina to deal with daily problems much better than on the days I do not exercise. I know that when I don't have sugar or much caffeine, I feel great and look better without them. That gives me the satisfaction that I was able to make the right choices for myself, which is enough motivation to change or affect my behavior on a daily basis. I find that if I look upon the benefits, one decision at a time, it is much easier to change habits or to change a point of view. Simply following through on good intentions, one by one, lets us reap their rewards.

That is a general sense of how I am motivated throughout my day, and I want to break it down into bite-sized pieces to help set expectations and create the space for change to occur.

Changing our beliefs starts with accepting the idea that we need to change what is not working for us and we will be better for making this change, as will all of those whose lives we affect.

When we implement the doctrine of taking preventative measures versus repairing damage that has already been done, we are on our way to optimal life.

When we finally realize we need a change, we have taken a look at our internal operating system and found it to be lacking. What it takes to change becomes apparent. One step at a time, they say, but the key components to change are the following:

❖ Recognizing our limiting beliefs.

❖ Willingness to change.

❖ Taking action to change.

❖ Creating an environment where change is supported.

❖ Creating a reward system.

Our ability to change resides within us and is available for our use when we become aware of our own limiting beliefs. It depends on our willingness to minimize self-interference; we can listen quietly to our own self-talk and act accordingly. With seasonal living, you are being asked to tune into your environment, body, and emotional state, as well as the foods, cosmetics, and the people you come into contact with.

Through self-awareness, you can tune into what you already

know, stop the interference, and make changes that will benefit your life physically, mentally, and emotionally. The first step, as mentioned earlier, is in our breath. We arrive in the world with our first breath, bringing ourselves present, and we leave after our last.

Most of us make choices based on our past beliefs or ideas. They manifest themselves as thoughts and feelings in our bodies and in all of our actions, the things we say, the things we buy, the decisions we make, and how we spend our time. Media exposure and what has been taught by or heard from others can create these stories. The important thing to note is how we have made the associations that shaped our beliefs. The chain of decisions recreates our habits.

Our choices are decisions that turn into behaviors. When we redefine our core beliefs, we can begin to experience ourselves as healthy, happy, loving, fulfilled, and emotionally balanced. To change, we must keep our eyes on the prize. We make contracts with ourselves, and our agreements are based on our past experiences, where many decisions have been fear-based or based on the needs of our ego. By consolidating the two and recognizing that neither one is our friend, we can then come to a place where our decisions have a gentle outcome for us and those around us.

Keep in mind that weak decisions create weak character,
leading us to dislike ourselves.

Making a Contract

This is the place to make a contract with yourself and begin your journey. You spend most of your time with yourself. We have the power to become what we ultimately want to be.

With regard to our overall living experience and how we see the world, this can be challenging at times. Going back to chemical-free and natural living is the way we maintain our lives; there is a difference. For emergencies and accidents, Western medicine is the best: it's miraculous at treating symptoms or life and death crises. However, Western medicine doesn't give us the recipe to prevent the causes of illness or live well on a day-to-day basis. It doesn't show us how to restore ourselves once something fails.

Once we have analyzed our core beliefs, we can use this simple reminder to keep ourselves on track with our self-commitment.

Our Actions Lead Us to Habits and a

Practice of Living

Once we have chosen a new direction and are committed to shifting our beliefs around health, the environment, and our actions, we can then carry them forward through application to our self-management of a lifestyle that embodies all that we possess and want to share with others.

Seasonal Tip:

Get to know yourself first by being completely honest by recognizing if what you want, what you say, and what you do are the same. Reconcile all three to be the same; express what you want and do it.

Understanding Our Habits and Practices Reduces Stress and Aging

When I become aware of myself, my environment, the season I am in, and of others, I can begin to understand my own place in the equation. I can now make room for change and realize that my health is the most important and truly the least expensive thing I have to maintain. This is when we must learn to ask ourselves before we do something if it will truly be good for us in the long run. We need to determine if a moment of instant pleasure is worth the long-term consequence.

I have adapted the system of this basic principle of what our needs are to achieve our potential and fulfillment. According to Abraham Maslow, an American psychologist, there are four layers of needs (beyond our basic physiological need for survival) that must be addressed in order for a person to feel at ease and complete. When the four secondary needs are out of balance, there may be no obvious physical manifestation, but the person will feel anxious or tense. This is not exactly true; in extreme cases, where it is clear the body does change chemically, it causes the resulting emotional distress (despite a lack of obvious physical signs). The survival instinct will ensure fulfillment of the primary physiological needs before it will focus on the secondary needs.

HIERARCHY OF OUR EXISTANCE

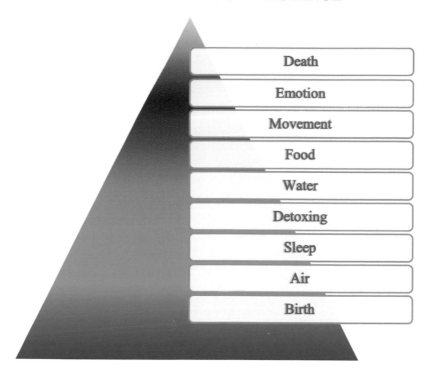

Changing your mood is part of changing your attitude.

A change of attitude creates new situations; new situations create new social settings leading to new relationships, both business and personal.

Seasonal Tip:

For the first month of creating new habits, make a list of how things make you feel when you eat them, put them on your skin, wear them, or experience them. Use these notes to adjust your habits.

Adapt a youthful attitude and try new
experiences. Opening yourself to change will
bring you more into alignment with seasonal living!

Improvement—Focus On Fabulous Living Through Feelings and Beliefs

As you make changes, notice the results. Even changing your mealtime to at least three hours before bed can make a huge improvement to your constitution and skin in just one day. Just taking a vitamin or using seasonal skin care can provide a healthier look in the mirror when you wake up, starting the day off positively. Giving more attention and respect to your self-care in dress, food, and thought will have people noticing you — and its benefits!

Being a Catalyst of Change

Prince Charles, a true Renaissance monarch, has developed 17 programs through his Prince of Wales Foundation. Here are a few of his accomplishments:

Photo by Royal Photographer

❖ Seven hundred and fifty thousand lives have been changed by giving young people skills, a new belief system, and self-esteem. He then designed a network of graduate-ambassadors for them to acquire employment.

❖ Giving new direction for self-employment to people over 50 who are deemed unemployable.

❖ Changing the architectural landscape by adapting it to its surroundings in sustainable buildings.

❖ Teaching organic farming and gardening methods.

❖ Teaching science through art.

❖ Teaching the value of art through history.

Please visit: **http://princes-foundation.org** for more information.

Seasonal Tip:

Living out your true inner desires is success in itself.

Reinforcement

Reinforcement is received by our self-perception and personal success, and it also comes in the form of positive feedback from others. This feedback can be direct, such as a compliment, or it can be indirect, where we notice (through awareness) how others are responding to our process of becoming more aware, taking better care of ourselves, and as a consequence, being more present with them. When you receive positive feedback, it is hard to resist the desire to give as well. This begins your positive cycle.

Be mindful; validation through reinforcement can be a trickster. We must always be aware that we are validating positive thoughts and positive actions; we are *not* feeding our ego, seeking toprevail at any cost. This is the time to reach for our moral beacons and stay true to our integrity and correct values.

Seasonal Tip:

A deep inhale every morning with the slow exhale of breath will ground you upon awaking as it is life's first signal to start the new day. This will make you feel full, aware, and present to approach the day.

Giving Back: Joy Makes You Younger

Feeding my adopted seal, Roxy at the Marine Mammal Center in Sausalito, California

Giving back builds community and support for common interests. It can be done in many ways by giving someone your time and attention, through service, fundraising, or just helping someone as we should.

At our nearby Marine Mammal Center, I sponsored a baby seal that was separated from its mother during a storm. My donation was in memory of my dog, Roxy, who died suddenly from heart failure.

I received great joy from feeding the young seal and watching her grow until she was ready to go back into the wild. It made me realize on a deeper level what it is to be a part of the environment and cycle of life. This is a good example how giving gives back. When we take part in these actions, we share our beliefs and ourselves. If we are doing well, then we exemplify health and balance that in turn attracts others to work toward the same goals. We show and share ourselves by example. It is hard not to smile back when someone smiles at you.

If you would like to know more about or donate to the **Marine Mammal Center**, please visit their website:

http://www.marinemammalcenter.org

Photo by Michael Kleeman

Our Time

The way we spend time in our lives and how we choose to absorb the moments that are offered to us is of importance. We're on this earth for a short time, and time is the most valuable commodity in existence. You can make money, you can lose money, you can make friends, you can lose friends, you can acquire business, and you can lose business—but you never get time back, so how we spend time and what it gives us in return is the most valuable thing we create.

There is no substitute for finding a place of belonging and a sense of true purpose. See change as furthering your life.

CHAPTER TWELVE - EMBRACING CHANGE

Travel In Comfort

For many of us, life is so busy that a long plane flight can be used as a time to be quiet. It can be filled with a good movie or book, or it can be used to get extra sleep. Prepare for your flight by planning your in-flight activity.

- ❖ Always have a cozy blanket with you as the air tends to become very cold.

- ❖ Fly without wearing makeup.

- ❖ Wear stylish, comfortable clothes that move with your body.

- ❖ Prepare your face by wetting it and applying sleep repair scrum to protect your skin from excessive air conditioning and altitude.

- ❖ Remove your shoes and put on soft socks for comfort.

- ❖ During a long flight, I use my **Replete Rejuvenating Mist**™ to hydrate the exposed skin.

- ❖ Reapply **Replete Lip Restore**™ to your lips and cuticles while on the flight.

❖ Make sure you have your toothpaste and toothbrush handy.

Once back at your home or hotel, soak in a warm bath for at least 20 minutes to rehydrate and reduce the effects of jet lag. At the first opportunity, spend 20 minutes in the sunlight (after 4 p.m.) for your brain to regulate your sleep pattern.

Theory without practice yields no fruit.

My Be Fabulous At Any Age Notes:

At home with Boris.

CHAPTER THIRTEEN

HARMONIZING YOUR LIVING SPACE

Constructing Your World

You can reinforce your new habits by constructing your world around them and implementing behaviors, products, clothing, foods, plants, and objects that support the shift. When you begin to do this with regularity, you will more easily fall into seasonal patterns and rhythms for yourself and your family.

Our Home

Create a place that you call home that you are eager to return to, where you can rejuvenate and recover from your busy day. Everything you surround yourself with should remind you that you are at home. This is where you get your strength to go out and make a contribution to your community and share with others. It motivates you from the inside out. You should find strength in your home, no matter the size. It does not need to be fancy or large or in some special city or place. It is where you are right now.

Creating an environment and quality of life specific to you is what the seasonal living philosophy is all about.

Sensual Smells

The sense of smell is one of our senses through which we connect to our outside surroundings. Each of us has many different sensors and stimuli that we respond to: visual (sight), auditory (hearing), gustatory perception (taste), olfaction (smell), somatic perception (touch), temperature, pain, and spatial comfort to name some. All fragrances have an impact on our systems, whether they are natural or synthetic.

The more the senses are stimulated, the better. They cause us to notice our environment and they invoke old stories and memories. The natural fragrance of earthy botanicals, such as roses, rosemary, lilac, peppermint, green teas, and fresh-cut wood or bark, help make us present, call out attention to, and eventually help recall the moment. A garden or pot of climbing jasmine can create an overall sense of well-being when we walk past it or when the scent drifts our way. Even the smell of fresh coffee has a different meaning than roasting coffee beans. As you walk through a garden, your senses are stimulated and they are developed. Real smells of real herbs, botanicals, and foods are significant in drawing out memories and meaning in our lives. There is no denying it. Manufactured products and their contrived scents do not offer the same benefits or have lasting, positive memory imprinting. It is clear that the scents of essential oils are very powerful for creating and changing moods.

Scents best harmonized with each season:

Spring–Vanilla, uplifting and comforting scent

Summer–Mint, cooling and refreshing

Autumn–Lavender, soothing and calming

Winter–Rosemary, preserving and antibacterial

Seasonal Tip:

Brighten the smell of your home throughout the year with dried herbs and flowers. Place rosemary and lavender between your linens; it will elevate your mood and make going to bed fun. Dried rose petals and lilac flowers are great scents too. Change them seasonally to your liking.

Organizing Your Work Environment

Our work environment is also very important, whether we work at home or in an office. Having plenty of light is important, as well as a good chair and no clutter. On your desk, place a plant or a couple of photos to remind you of positive experiences, family, or goals.

Photo by Liza Gershman

The Value of Gardens

In my own formal garden, I am fortunate to have many fruit trees: peach, apple, cherries, and citrus with sunflowers on both sides. I grow tomatoes and vegetables, as well as herbs. When I leave my kitchen and inhale the rich smells of the garden, the herbs, flowers, and the tall cypress trees that sit above the house, I know I am home and I feel grounded in that thought. Beauty must be incorporated into our daily lives. Think about what will make your environment and living space beautiful and comfortable. Use your space and update it for every season.

Chemical-free, natural gardening supports the cycles of nature. When we have plants, fruit trees, herbs, and fresh root vegetables growing in our yards, garden, and landscaping around our homes, we are supporting the natural cycle and the environment as well as ourselves. For myself, I plan in advance to leave half of the harvest for the animals and birds to feed on. I do this intentionally so I can watch them thrive. I receive great satisfaction and am grateful to be able to witness this. This process is the cycle of life, and it is incredibly important to implement some aspect of this into our daily lives at whatever level we can. Even if you live in the city, you can still place a pot of herbs and vegetables in your window. You can sprout beans and seeds in a small bowl next to your kitchen sink. It is inherent in us and in all things to grow. The wonder of it keeps us youthful, sustained, and nourished.

Everything in nature is governed by its own set of laws and of opposites. For example, when you plant things in your garden, you must consider location, environment, and which ones can be close together and which ones cannot. Plants in the nightshade family like potatoes, bell peppers, tomatoes or eggplants, should not be planted next to pumpkins, raspberries, squashes, cucumbers or sunflowers. This is also true of our interaction among people. We all have a purpose and place in this world, and at times, we find ourselves without support to thrive. This should remind us to move on to a more fertile environment that will be more cooperative or symbiotic for us.

We thrive when we are surrounded by people who support us, want us to become the best we can be, and will help develop our lives to the fullest without limits. You may wonder what this looks like. It is very simple. Just like the plants, some people protect us from invasions by others and stress or physical harm, or they support us in our times of need and don't leave us when we are weak. They provide the fertile soil of deep relationships, allowing us to grow, expand, and come back stronger every season. It is also quickly clear that there are other types who inhibit and poison our lives' progress, and like potatoes, they should grow away from the rest of the crop amongst their own kind.

Seasonal Tip:

Do not try to force things. Nature tells us that there is no symbiotic living with a potato unless you are one. Move on to compatible environments.

Let the Vivid Colors of Flowers Brighten Your Day

Appreciating our environment, remembering to contribute to it, and being in harmony with the seasons are what make our lives fulfilling on every level. You can feel beauty walking through your yard, through your house, or anywhere you can grow something. Create focal points of beauty that are soothing, meaningful, and encouraging to you. Each will actually affect you differently each time you walk by and notice them. Even an empty space has an effect on you and serves its own purpose if you create it intentionally. Placing seasonal flowers or meaningful objects in the kitchen or around the house brings beauty and life inside.

Seasonal Tip:

Fill a summer fruit basket with squash in the autumn and pine cones in the winter. In the spring, grow flowering bulbs in a glass bowl.

Our Purchases and Decisions

We all should strive in a natural way to acquire quality products for our home. There are times where we need to make decisions regarding our purchasing goals. At times, we need to ask if our desires are in line with our living needs and our senses. We know we have arrived when we can combine necessity, function, and luxury into one and the same.

Beautiful Living That Echoes the Seasons

❖ **Spring**– In the spring, it is natural to want to purge and clean out the things that have gathered in stagnation during the winter. We air out our homes, clear out our closets, and prepare our gardens for growth. We amend our soil, then plant annuals, herbs, and seeds. It is the perfect time to go through our closets and change over our seasonal wardrobe. This is an exercise we need to implement for each season. During this time, our cells begin their expansive stage, and we start to desire foods that echo this change, like salads and fresh produce.

❖ **Summer**– We socialize through many outdoor activities. We travel around the globe to experience different foods, customs and surroundings. This is the time we enjoy water sports and fill ourselves with stimulation and adventure. The interior of our homes should reflect the light and airiness of the summer by using white and happy colors.

❖ **Autumn**– In autumn, we become more contemplative and begin to mentally prepare for the winter and the end of the year. We begin doing things that make us more productive and creative. During this time, we also accumulate and hold on to the necessary nutrients from our food, skin care, air, water, and supplements, because in the winter, nutrients are scarce. Our bodies are programmed primarily to use our stored nutrients and do not look to obtain them from the outside. The autumn season is the most important season to heed.

❖ **Winter**– Designing your visual and physical space is of utmost importance as we spend the majority of our time indoors. Put effort into creating a reading area that contains visual and physical surroundings ready to please your senses. Think of flowers, candles, blankets, and music that you love. This is when we need to use our clothes and interior decorating as an additional aid to feeling good. We need richer foods to support our hormone-elevated state and root foods to complement the contracted winter cells in our body.

Seasonal positive ideas, actions, and thoughts:

- Awareness—requires an assignment of intent.

- Create an atmosphere of beauty.

- Think quality over quantity.

- Stay organized for today.

- Open up and become more aware of your environment.

- Notice when you feel good, when you are happy, when your skin seems smooth, or when it is inflamed.

- Look around and take mental notes of your natural environment.

❖ Take a note of the current season.

❖ Involve yourself in the moment for what the season represents. It will give you the feeling of traveling and coming back with renewed attitude.

❖ Enjoy the colors that seasons bring by filling your surroundings with them.

❖ Let feelings of gratitude fill you up when you come home after a long day of work or errands, allowing stress to fade away.

❖ Try doing something different.

❖ Start with a morning shower.

❖ Get dressed as if it is important.

❖ Prepare your meals as though they have meaning–they truly do!

❖ Everything we do affects us.

❖ How do you feel about your home comforts when your bathroom is cluttered or clear? Whichever makes you feel more comfortable to live with should be the one you put effort into.

❖ Create beauty around you in your home, your yard, or on your kitchen table with fruits or flowers. For me, even a small display on my kitchen table, in a nook, or on my desk is esthetically gratifying and spiritually uplifting.

❖ Find a way to feel in sync with the season. It will prove to be consistently uplifting for you.

My Be Fabulous At Any Age Notes:

Photo by Liza Gershman

CHAPTER FOURTEEN

SEASONAL PERSONAL FASHION

Fashion & Style

Fashion gives us opportunity to express our individuality by presenting examples of the feelings we want to share through wearable art. Style is a fully developed message confirming our established personality. The difference between trendy and style is that trendy lasts only a season and does not express who we are or how we feel. Trends follow someone else's expression and their state of mind. Style, on the other hand, is a mature, evolved, polished, rounded, and consistent theme through which an individual continues to express her own moods without losing her individuality in the fashion world. People who have personal style always have something to wear in their closets; their pieces of wardrobe can easily be matched with one another. When you buy quality and have a few pieces of the top-level brands, you will find that they last much longer because of the attention to detail.

Part of our evolving is the ability to find our own voice in what we wear and comfort in having one's own style. Every season, you can acquire a complementary addition, instead of disjoined pieces of clothing that will remain untouched. It is much better to buy a few items that are classics and can be mixed and matched. You will be calmer and be more efficient as you prepare for your day or special events.

Wear what you feel good in; that is the key. Notice how each garment expresses your mood and fits your shape, and how the texture of the fabric connects with your skin. Fabrics should never be irritating; you do not want to preoccupy your mind with itching, then wiggling to avoid it. They should be functional, keep your body temperature comfortable, and feel soothing on your skin. Make sure your clothes are clean, pressed, and appropriate for each occasion.

Photo by Liza Gershman

Seasonal Tip:

Go into your closet and pull out your absolute favorites for every occasion—*that* is your style. Determine color, consistency, and accessories. You will then have a wardrobe that will take you anywhere you want to go by adding to it year after year.

Women's Shoes

Shoes are the most sensual part of our wardrobe. It is said that people who pay great attention to shoes are more sexual than others. Maybe there is something to it. We have shoes like Mary Janes; we have shoes with little peek-a-boos, and we have shoes that just show a tiny part of the toes and nothing else. I guess they can be teasers to our nakedness. After all, if they didn't have such a strong impact on our sexuality, why on earth would we own so many of them and pay so much for them? Quality shoes will last for years. Buy the best based on fit, weight distribution, then appearance. It is most important that the feet are not stressed, cramped, or bent with discomfort. The angle of the shoes will determine your spine alignment. How they feel to walk in will determine if you are rested or tired at the end of the day.

Seasonal Tip:

I have found that my greatest enjoyment is to be able to wear beautiful shoes with great comfort. I change my shoes three times a day to change the pressure points of my weight, so my feet and spine alignment never become stressed. This way, no matter the heel, my legs get great excrcise, and my feet don't mind it. After all, high-heeled shoes are a big part of our feminine side.

Men's Shoes

Some men may think that their shoes don't matter. The truth is in some instances, they matter more, because men have fewer options to express their personality through style than women. Their shoes send out strong messages as to who they are and what they care about.

Seasonal Tip:

Always buy your shoes in the afternoon and buy half a size larger shoes for late-evening outings. This will assure your comfort no matter what activities you are engaging in.

The seasons should be the foremost consideration when choosing shoes. Wearing shoes has been dictated by seasonal changes for ages.

Seasonal Tip:

Buy the best quality of shoes in your style and for comfort and longevity.

Gemstones

Photo by Liza Gershman

Ever since I was a little girl, I was always attracted to gems. I loved the brilliant colors and their depth. As I looked into them, I expected to find meaning and had the sense they would give me special powers. To me, the gems were a source of great mystery. Whether they were marbles, semi-precious stones, or even precious stones, we played games with them. People did not assign them the monetary value as they do today. They were looked upon as family heirlooms. The strength of their attraction has never waned.

As my curiosity about them continued, I tried to find the answers as to what was giving them so much mystery, power, and value, only to finally find the connection between them and us on my last expedition into the jungle while working with medicine men.

Our DNA coding language is based on a four-letter alphabet (ATCG) and the DNA structure is a crystal one, similar to how precious stones are formed. Closest to our DNA is the crystalline formation of quartz. Interestingly enough, quartz crystals are used by medicine men as amplifiers to heal their patients! Is this coincidence or old knowledge though trial and error? It became clear to me that DNA language codes our intentions, and crystal formations are emitting and receiving signals. These are then amplified from one DNA to another, which is how all living things communicate over distance and with words in DNA language.

This is how we are all connected and trends are created among us. This is what our heart reads—the intention—before we apply any of our other senses.

Pearls worn against the skin become more lustrous and beautiful.

Pearl dust is part of my botanical formula, acting as a sunscreen, as it did for Queen Cleopatra.

When we think of gemstones and consider what we will be wearing or buying, we may consider the best quality stone, and then we should choose their purpose, either for supporting our health or to be beautiful family heirlooms for generations to come. Aside from their magnetic powers, the monetary value of gemstones and jewelry has served many families well in times of crises or need when they were in survival mode, left with nothing but heirlooms to sustain themselves with. Gems were often used to barter with in exchange for their lives during crisis. Their significance resonates with their undeniable energy and how they are perceived. Gemstones are believed to relate to the position of the planets and their positive and negative effects. Each of us has a gemstone assigned with us at birth, which is also representative of the month we were born in and more. The very first use of gemstones was in medicine. They were crushed into powder and consumed. Later, it was discovered that by wearing them as healing stones, the medicinal effects were the same, and their value was further increased. This led to placing the stones in mountings to be worn as jewelry. Eventually, the jewelry itself would come to be the point of identity for the wearer. Consider where gemstones come from, how they were formed, and that they are proven to contain electromagnetic energy vibration. The use of gems in modern science, computer technology, watches, lasers, and electronic devices only illustrates their power and importance. Is that coincidence too, or is it just a part in their applications?

The more subtle power of gemstones to aid in healing processes and help balance human emotions has not been defined by modern science. Although gems are rare and beautiful, their allure is directly related to the power they provide when worn. This is transmitted through contact with your body.

Wearing jewelry and gemstones is as good for our health, energy, and vitality as it is a fashion statement. It is not a coincidence that people wear them, cut them into different shapes, pass them on for generations, and hold them in high regard. For the most part, that has less to do with financial value than some sense of the unknown they contain. For example, aquamarine, a stone of communications, should be given as a wedding gift between the husband and wife to assure good communication flow during the marriage. A diamond is given as an engagement gift to represent and assist in their love, withstanding life's pressures, as it is the hardest stone known to us.

This type of quality has been assigned to gemstones from hundreds of years of observations by different cultures and sciences. They somehow agree as to the properties they represent. Astrology has each month of the year attributed to a specific gem.

Month	Stone	Properties	Medicinal Value
January	Garnet	Faithful	Stimulate Pituitary Gland
February	Amethyst	Spiritual Balance	Prevent Intoxication
March	Aquamarine	Purification	Promotes Healthy Cell Growth
April	Diamond	Strength	Healer of Physical Complaints
May	Emerald	Personal Growth	Supports Spine & Nerve Column
June	Pearl	Purity	Heal Intestinal tract
July	Ruby	Health	Heart Support
August	Peridot	Good Fortune	Used to Cure Asthma
September	Sapphire	Honesty	Healing
October	Opal	Innocence	Cure Eye Diseases
November	Topaz	Courage	Stabilizing
December	Turquoise	Prosperity	Cure Stomach Disorders

(Disclaimer: this is not intended as medical advice, but as a reference to historical beliefs and uses of gems for their healing attributes.)

Seasonal Tip:

Wear your gemstones to benefit from their healing powers.

CHAPTER FIFTEEN

SEASONAL TRAVEL

Travel Destinations

Here are some suggestions:

Country	Best Time to Visit
Africa – Kenya http://www.lonelyplanet.com/kenya	Game viewing is at its best in mid-summer (after rainy season). Days are long and the weather pleasant. Best month: July.
Amsterdam http://www.iamsterdam.com/en-GB/Experience	Spring is most beautiful; weather is warm and clear, the tulips are in full bloom and tourists haven't arrived yet.
Australia – Melbourne http://www.visitmelbourne.com	March to May. Whatever time you travel there, take clothes for almost any season; the winds can bring sudden changes of temperatures.
Australia – Sydney http://www.sydney.com	April to June (Australian Autumn). City is at its exuberant best (before crowds and humidity are too much to bear).

Country	Best Time to Visit
Belgium – Brussels http://visitbrussels.be	With cool summers and mild winters, it's an ideal city-break destination year-round.
Denmark – Copenhagen http://www.copenhagen.com/tourism/welcome.asp	Spring is ideal, warm, and comfortable (tourists haven't arrived yet). If you like jazz, the annual Copenhagen Jazz Festival starts on the first Friday of July and features approximately 450 concerts over 10 days.
Finland – Helsinki http://www.visithelsinki.fi/en	Summers are short but warm. (mid-June to mid-August)
Germany – Berlin http://www.lonelyplanet.com/germany/berlin	Between May and October is the city's most reliable weather period.
Greece – Athens www.greece-athens.com	Most pleasant in spring or early summer and autumn before and after the tourist rush in July and August. Temperatures can be extreme during the summer or winter.
India – Mumbai http://www.mumbai.org.uk	Best between September and April; the city is relatively dry and cool.
Ireland – Dublin http://www.visitdublin.com	Spring and autumn are less busy with tourists.
Italy – Lake Como http://www.discovercomo.com	May through September.
Italy – Rome http://www.turismoroma.it/?lang=en	Spring (tourists have yet to arrive). Autumn is also good; less oppressive heat than summer.

Country	Best Time to Visit
Italy – Venice http://www.venice-tourism.com/en/visit-venice.html	November is at its emptiest and most atmospheric. January is also good between the mini-peak of Christmas and the tourist-oriented Carnevale in late February or early March.
Japan - Tokyo http://www.gotokyo.org/en/index.html	Spring is best from March to May. Early April is the cherry blossom season. Tokyo is at its liveliest then with hanami (cherry blossom viewing) parties in the parks. Avoid summer when it's hot and muggy.
London http://www.visitlondon.com	Great year-round. Warmest in August. Coldest in February.
Malta http://www.visitmalta.com	Avoid in spring, sirocco winds bake the islands. Go in summer when they are cooled by sea breezes. Best month is probably August, although if you can't take the heat, go in July when it's milder.
Paris http://en.parisinfo.com	Beautiful in spring. Fun to visit on France's national Bastille Day, July 14; the storming of the Bastille is commemorated with a massive fireworks display and party in the streets.
Philippines http://itsmorefuninthephilippines.com	Visit during dry season, January to June. Peak tourist dates are Christmas, New Year, Chinese New Year, and Easter.

Country	Best Time to Visit
Poland – Krakow http://www.krakow.pl/english	Early autumn is their cultural season. Great continental city without the tourist hordes. Spring is also good, when mild weather allows for excellent outdoor activities.
Poland – Mazury http://www.poland.travel/en/cities-towns/gizycko-welcome-to-the-mazury	Beautiful interconnected lakes, fantastic for all water sports; great food too. May through July. Excellent ski sports in winter.
Poland – Poznan http://www.poznan.pl/mim/public/turystyka/index.html?lang=en http://www.maltaski.pl/	An International Trade Center with great winter sports, voted 2012 Travelers choice winner – Destinations. The host of many world conferences, Poznan is quickly becoming a global city. It is also home to Malta Lake, a man-made lake with a year-round ski complex.
Portugal – Lisbon http://www.golisbon.com/	Late summer has sultry weather (and quiet) or late spring has warm days, cool
Romania – Bucharest http://www.romaniatourism.com/bucharest.html	Go in autumn to enjoy this city's Parisian-like charms. Summer rains have ended and it's still warm enough to eat outside. Best month is probably October.
Russia – St. Petersburg http://st-petersburg.ru/en/Pages/Home.aspx	High season (music festivals and other cultural events = lots of tourists) in June. Good alternatives are spring (April

Country	Best Time to Visit
Russia – St. Petersburg (contd)	to May) and autumn (September to October). Avoid November to March and July and August (swamp-like time with plagues of mosquitoes). Winter is beautiful for sights and romantic troika rides (best month is February for this).
Scotland - Edinburgh http://www.edinburgh.org/	For the best weather (though that's not its main attraction), go between May and September. July and August are the city's busiest months for Edinburgh Festival.
South Africa – Cape Town http://www.capetown.travel/	Avoid tourist influx during December and January. Bad weather September – November.
South Africa – Johannesburg http://www.joburgtourism.com	Spring is best (September – November) for wildflowers in the Northern and Western Cape provinces. Summer (November to April) can be uncomfortably hot. Winters are mild.
South Africa – Kruger Natl. Park http://www.sanparks.org/parks/kruger	May – September (dry season). Best time for game-viewing; animals can be seen at waterholes. Anticipate cool mornings and warm days.

Country	Best Time to Visit
South America – Belize http://www.travelbelize.org	At its best between September and May. Dry season runs from November to May; wet season from June to October. Beautiful country of coral reefs (Meso-American barrier reef), sapphire seas, great Mayan history and understatedly slick resorts.
South America – Costa Rica http://www.visitcostarica.com	Best time to go is during the coffee harvest, December to January (coincides with the high season, which begins around 20 December, when flights and hotels book up rapidly through to February.) Some hotels shut down for September and October, the rainiest months.
South America – The Amazon http://www.colombia.travel/en	Close to the equator, so climate stays the same year-round. Rainy season runs from November to March, and while soggy, it can be the best time to see caimans and other large river species. You can also travel further by boat then. Conversely, the dry season is the best time to explore the Várzea.
Spain – Barcelona http://www.lonelyplanet.com/ spain/barcelona	Visit during their mild spring and autumn. Avoid during the high summer in July and August when atmospheric pollution is high.

Country	Best Time to Visit
Spain – Madrid http://www.esmadrid.com/en/portal.do	Early summer: city is buzzing and the weather isn't as stifling as in July and August.
Sweden – Stockholm http://www.visitstockholm.com/en/	Most beautiful in winter, but don't go if you're afraid of the cold! July and August have the clearest weather.
Swedish Lapland – Ice Hotel http://www.icehotel.com/	A once-in-a-lifetime experience, this wondrous ice hotel is built yearly between December and April. It features many themed rooms by different artists. Also has a wedding chapel for the adventurous.
Switzerland – St. Moritz http://www.cntraveller.com/guides/europe/switzerland/st-moritz/where-to-stay	Ski season runs from December to April. Summer season from mid-June to mid-October. It's the oldest winter sports resort in the world and the most glamorous Alpine retreat.
Switzerland – Zurich http://www.myswitzerland.com/en/zurich.html	In April, temperatures begin to rise, trees are in bloom, and there is still snow in nearby ski resorts. Zurich has recently undergone a massive explosion in arts and popular culture. Known as the cleanest and most efficient city in Europe.
Vienna, Austria http://www.wien.info/en	Summer is best (always a chance of rain). Winters can be bitterly cold.

Photo by Liza Gershman

CHAPTER SIXTEEN

SEASONAL LIVING FOR
AGELESS BEAUTY

We are the sum of our environment and experience, and how we choose to use them. Ultimately, our character is displayed by the sum of information we obtain.

Seasonal living is about embracing a seasonal lifestyle and philosophy in every aspect of your mental, physical, and emotional being. We can go through each year with complacency or we can align with the natural cycles of the seasons. Embracing the life we create and maintaining it through renewal is critical for long-term impacts on ourselves and others. We do this by making sure that we stick to fresh, chemical-free food; we also use the best quality products for our skin, bodies, homes, and families.

It is clear that food is only one source of nourishment. Social relationships, emotions, music, paintings, art, culture, and beautiful views from our homes or other places are all our food for thought and body. If one is to achieve optimum health, a *great life* involves a balance of all components of seasonal living. Our goal is to age gracefully, but not prematurely, and if possible, defy aging through constant care of ourselves without allowing our nutrients to be depleted. Aging happens because we use up nutrients without replacing them; our brain then shuts down peripheral systems, which are aspects of attractiveness. Some of the obvious peripherals to shut down are hair, skin, nails, smell, sight, and the last is a changing of the voice. As these go, we start to lose our ability to attract a mate.

We have talked about the main attributes and concerns of our bodies, our skin, and our physical and emotional health, and how it is affected by our environment in *Be Fabulous at Any Age: Creating Ageless Skin Through Seasonal Living*. We have also talked about making changes and what it takes to make a fundamental, paradigm-shifting change permanent. Once you have decided to make a change, you can support yourself by making it a lifestyle choice. This enforces the change and compounds your positive results in an ongoing fashion. This is the beauty of choice; choice is something that we grant ourselves every time we make a decision. This decision is about who we are, who we want to become, and what we are willing to let go of in the process. We decide how we want to treat and show respect to others, and how we want to be treated and respected too. We can apply this to our relationship with nature and ourselves, including what self-care products we use and how much we sleep.

Ageless Longevity

Ageless longevity means our quality of life continues in a stable, peaceful way, in a state of balance and optimal health. For ageless beauty inside and out, you must first consider your health as we have discussed. Your mental, physical, and emotional health are dependent on your seasonal self-care. Your skin is your social calling card; it either attracts or repels. Ageless longevity is the theory of living out a fruitful life, to die healthy and peacefully of old age, rather than in deterioration. Our aging is directly related to loss of nutrients and *not* the passage of time. Our physical body's regeneration processes depend on availability of building blocks necessary for repair and replacement of cells.

Find and Develop Seasonal Activities

Seasonal activities align us with seasonal change; they develop traditions for our children and bring families closer together. Seasonal activities make us aware of the changes that are happening around us and allow us to prepare and move into them smoothly with grace. Traditions passed on for generations automatically align us with the cycle of seasons and change. These activities provide a foundation for reliability and order in our minds and our behaviors, thereby grounding us in our natural environment for accepting the natural order of the world as we prepare for change. Seasonal activities include games, travel, exploring nature, family meals, home decorating changes, changes in diet, shopping for different seasonally appropriate clothing, and creating small spaces inside your home by bringing the outside into it. Whether it is including autumn leaves and twigs for a display of the season, displaying fresh flowers in spring, or decorating with dried grasses in the summer, create more awareness for you and your family. You are creating an environment rich in color, depth, and awareness in which you and your family can thrive.

Art

This is where people found the need to create arts. We have so many mediums of expression that impact us. There is a clear distinction between the choices we make when choosing contact with art. We all have arts we support, whether as patrons, admirers, or participants. This can be a clear indicator of which form of art has the greatest effect on us. Arts provide a needed stimulation to our brain that in turn stimulates other glands and centers, which are responsible for our satisfaction and motivation.

This is why I have assigned corresponding arts to six senses. Knowing this will help us to find our balancing aspects for our systems and lives.

Introducing the Family to Nature

Seasonal Sports and Play. Engaging in play, whether it is outdoor play in the summer or snow fights in the winter, invigorates the mind and the senses. We stimulate ourselves and engage in competitive activities through play and sports. You learn more about relationships, sportsmanship, and structure when you engage in seasonal sports. There is seasonal play for everyone with games we play indoors and outdoors.

Tennis is a great outdoor seasonal sport.

Whether we play quietly or physically, we address facets of our personal needs, then recognize and nourish them. If we do not, we are off-balance and emotions and stress can build up inside of us and be released in inappropriate ways. Ancient Greeks and Romans embraced play and consumption, in extreme ways for sure, but it was a part of the time and preparation for the extreme trials of living. We can create balance by addressing those needs as they occur.

Taking Time for Seeing Friends and Having Pets

Photo by Drew Altizer

Photo by Andres Szabo

Putting effort into seeing your friends, regardless of the distance, gives us the continuity of friendships we build during our lifetime. It provides the heart with safe places to go to. They are great partners in sports, social games, and having fun.

Boris

Pets are a great way to take focus off yourself to care for others, especially if you do not have a spouse, kids, or family. Pets provide laughter and can calm and soothe you any time. They come for love, and they give love unconditionally. Having pets is a way of taking care of yourself as you take care of them. It keeps the continuum of care going. My pets encourage walks and enjoyment of the outdoors during times I might have ignored the need to step away from work. They follow their own natural rhythms and encourage you to do the same. Pets are known to extend the lives of their owners an average of five years. They reduce stress, help ground us, and make us more present as we step outside ourselves to attend to their needs. Enjoying time with pets is a wonderful way to relax.

Photo by Liza Gershman

FAREWELL

While I consider all those who came before me, have been my teachers, and have sparked interest in my quests, I know it is also my responsibility to go out and light the flame in others. I hope that I have accomplished this with my passion and philosophy in *Be Fabulous At Any Age: Creating Ageless Skin Through Seasonal Living.*

The continuity of seasonal living was lost during the years of conflict, such as the First and Second World Wars, when focus was placed on survival and not on thriving. This is how the cycle of passing on the wisdom of daily living ceased. Many of us still live by reaction to fear passed on by previous generations. Luckily, we are now open to living with coherent intention from the heart and not reacting to fear. We live in an exciting time of change and have the opportunity to go back to the basics. My inspiration and philosophy are born from deeply held values that took root from my formative years and my family's healthy lifestyle choices. I am committed to creating formulas based on natural plant extracts to reduce the appearance of daily stresses and the passage of time on our skin.

When I meet people who are vivacious and younger than their biological age, I discover that this is because they live by some of the principles I have shared with you here, therefore confirming its validity.

Of my teachers and the sources that I learned from, the way we need to maintain ourselves seems so obvious that I wonder how it happened that we allowed ourselves to be pulled so far astray. Scientists, philosophers, and healers all over the world and sprinkled throughout time have laid the groundwork for us. We are now at a place where global access and resourcing ability is at our fingertips, and collective wisdom has the opportunity to reach those who are interested in achieving the benefits of seasonal living and ageless longevity.

We are the managers of our lives and we influence those around us. It is an honor to have been given the gift of life; however, it is our choice how we live it. My return to seasonal living has made a huge effect on my life, and I hope you will thrive with the same rewards. Enjoy!

Elisabeth Thieriot

Our intentions affect everything we do and everyone we know.

Dear Elisabeth ---

A hIgh mark
of tides
that tell my life

speak softly
so I can hear from
what lives above

the crowning jewel
that travels clean
upon the spire
of earthly pleasures
--- the hinge pin
in Heaven's gate

Your particular palace
stands alone and free.

I play with abandon
into its lofty halls
as though I were
100 times the musician
I could ever hope to be,

but with the singular duty
the bugler musters at dawn
to summon the living
and the heroes gone

glenn woodruff

Appendix A

FOOD CONSUMPTION GUIDELINES

While your diet should not be severely strict, you should divide the foods you eat into percentages of daily intake and maintain a list of foods that should be avoided or only eaten sparingly. Fish and consumption of animal products are recommended, but can be easily modified. Have one three-course meal a day; keep other items separate. For your first meal, you can have soup (autumn and winter) or salads (spring and summer) with fruit as an afternoon snack. Take your main meal with protein and vegetables at dinner. If you have a big lunch, then just reverse the meals and have a small dinner. Your goal is to have only one three-course meal spread throughout the day. This will assure digestion without conflicts, and will keep your weight steady.

(Note: all foods can be substituted for ethnic foods with same properties.)

Follow the rule of three: Three food components, vegetables

with protein, carbohydrates with fruits, and dairy with fruits and nuts, and no more than three spices and flavorings on them. Never combine fruits with vegetables. This will keep your digestive tract ready to absorb the most nutrients and without bloating.

Carbohydrates (bread, pasta, rice, cereals, etc.) should ideally make up 10 percent of your diet and should represent a separate meal away from proteins and vegetables. Combine them with fruits and occasional cheese or butter.

Vegetables, including beans, should make up 60 percent of your diet. They should be lightly cooked, unless you have a digestive system strong enough to handle raw food. Choose vegetables in winter that are closest to the ground (in their most *contracted* state). In summer, eat food that is furthest from the ground (in their most *expanded* state). Use sparingly or avoid nightshade vegetables like potatoes, tomatoes, and eggplant because they affect our pH and make our system more acidic. In an acidic environment, we are more likely to develop cancer cells, diabetes, and many types of skin conditions. Keeping our system more alkaline is preferred, I find it works wonders.

In an alkaline environment, our skin functions smoothly without breakouts. The same skin in an acidic environment will develop rashes, pimples, and ulcerations; for that reason, keeping our body pH regulated is very important. The body is constantly doing its job ridding itself of toxins, but the environment that our organs perform in determine how efficiently that is accomplished.

VEGETABLES:

Have a variety of vegetables with each meal.

Use often:

Green leafy: Carrot tops, leeks, Collard greens, dandelion greens, Chinese cabbage, daikon greens, spring onions, Bok Choy, kale, mustard greens, watercress, parsley, turnip greens.

Round: Acorn squash, buttercup squash, broccoli, butternut squash, Italian cabbage, cauliflower, Brussels sprouts, romaine lettuce, onion, pumpkin and pumpkin seeds, red cabbage, turnips, chanterelle mushrooms, shiitake mushrooms.

Roots: Burdock, parsnip, carrots, lotus root, celery root, dandelion roots, radishes, daikon root, beets, taro, sweet potato, and yams.

Sea vegetables (Seaweed): Nori, wakame, Kombu, hiziki, arame, dulse and agar-agar. These all provide important vitamins and minerals.

Other: okra, bamboo shoots, rhubarb, squash, asparagus, zucchini, and peas.

Use occasionally:

Cucumber, chives, endive, snow peas, kohlrabi, celery, French green peas, Jerusalem artichoke, green beans, iceberg lettuce, mushrooms, sprouts, snap beans.

BEANS:

Do not eat beans more than once a day. It is best to combine six or more kinds at once.

Use often:

Chickpeas, azuki beans, and brown, red or green lentils.

Use occasionally:

Black-eyed peas, kidney beans, mung beans, lima beans, pinto beans, navy beans, whole dried peas, split peas.

FRUITS

Cooked: Cook your fruits in late autumn and winter or use dried or fresh, seasonal fruits two to three times a week.

Use often:

Tree Fruit: Cherries, apples, peaches, apricots, grapes, plums, tangerines, pears, avocado.

Ground Fruit: Blackberries, blueberries, honeydew melon, strawberries, raspberries, watermelon.

Tropical Fruits: Coconut, figs, papaya, citrus fruit, dates, mango, and pineapple.

WHOLE GRAINS

Use often:

Whole grains are best when cooked. Medium-grain and long-grain brown rice should be used in the Southern Hemisphere; barley, short-grain brown rice in the Northern Hemisphere; quinoa, millet, Spelt, fresh corn, whole oats, buckwheat, rye, pearl barley, whole wheat berries, sweet brown rice should be consumed according to your geographic location and season.

Flaked and cracked grains can be used in soups.

Use occasionally:

Sweet rice, bulgur, rolled oats, couscous, polenta, rye bread, corn grits, rye flakes, amaranth, and barley flakes.

FLOUR PRODUCTS

Use occasionally:

Whole-wheat noodles, buckwheat noodles, bread, sourdough breads, thin wheat noodles, homemade pancakes.

ADDING SEASONINGS TO YOUR FOODS

Use often:

Sea salt

Use occasionally:

Tamari, ginger, garlic, plum paste, brown rice vinegar, wasabi, and macadamia oil and avocado oil.

MILD HERBS, SPICES, OILS AND OTHER FOODS:

Use as needed:

Cucumber brined pickles, lemons, butter, olive oil, grape seed oil, natural sauerkraut, horseradish, coconut oil, butter, safflower oil. Use living water to cook with if possible, then apply healthy oil(s) after cooking to benefit most from them. Vinegars are also seasonings and balancers. Use balsamic vinegar, rice vinegars, cherry vinegar, and apple cider vinegar.

BEVERAGES:

Drink a comfortable amount of liquids for thirst; use natural herbal and black teas that have different effects on your body and brain. Some teas make you talkative, some make you sleepy, some are digestives, and some are for balance. Choose your teas based on your desire of the moment. Use spring water. I find that coffee has different effects on different people. This is evident because some people can maintain their weight with coffee while others gain weight. Decide what the best choice for your health is. It might be as subtle as different coffee beans or tea leaves that work best for your system. Consider the oils on the roasted beans.

Use often:

Almond milk, brown rice milk, grape juice, apple juice, coconut milk, carrot juice, other vegetable juices, herbal teas, and carbonated water.

Use occasionally:

Natural unfiltered beer.

MEAT:

Use occasionally:

Fish, lamb, eggs, bison, beef, chicken. Consume two or three times a week.

SEEDS & NUTS:

Eat as much of the following as you can hold in the palm of your hand at a time: sunflower seeds, pumpkin seeds, chestnuts, walnuts, peanuts, pecans, cashews, Brazil nuts, almonds, hazelnuts, pistachio nuts, macadamia nuts.

Nut Spreads: almond butter and sesame butter in moderation.

SWEETENERS:

For sweetening snacks or for baking or cooking, use brown rice syrup, barley malt, grape juice, apple juice, pure maple syrup, brown sugar, and honey. Avoid white sugar; use fructose instead. Eat the local honey wherever you may travel. It will lower your susceptibility to allergies.

BAKED/PROCESSED GRAINS

Use sparingly:

Baked flour goods, pastries, refined grains, cookies, rice cakes, puffed whole grains, commercial pasta, puffed cereals, muffins, commercial-pancakes, chips, baked pastries, popcorn, commercial pasta, white rice, and bread.

ABSTAIN FROM THE FOLLOWING IF POSSIBLE:

Dairy products—yogurt, milk, cheese, and ice cream.

Sweeteners—processed, artificial and white sugar.

Beverages—artificial beverages, iced drinks, cold drinks, hard liquor, distilled water, and stimulant beverages.

APPENDIX A

STYLES OF COOKING

Use often:

Boiling, pressure cooking, blanching, quick oil sautéing, steaming, soup-making, stewing, sautéing, quick water sautéing, simmering, pickling, and pressing.

Use occasionally:

Broiling, baking, dry roasting, deep-frying, tempura, juicing, and raw foods.

SHOPPING TIPS/LIST

❖ Buy chemical-free food as much as possible.

❖ Always buy whole grains when possible, not refined grains, and choose brown rice not white. Choose whole wheat for bread and pasta.

❖ Eat fresh vegetables at every meal.

❖ Unrefined sea salt, unrefined sesame, sunflower and coconut oils or avocado oil.

❖ Jams without sugar. Fruit juices without sugar.

❖ Replace sugar with honey, rice, and barley malt syrups as natural sweeteners.

❖ White-meat fish is preferred over red meats and chicken.

❖ For your proteins, try eggs and nuts, instead of cheese and meats when you can.

❖ Choose non-stimulating grain coffees and teas as much as possible, and use chemical-free coffee roasted in light oil as a balancer and mood elevator in moderation.

❖ Use sea vegetables when cooking as sources of calcium, B-12, and beta-carotene. They contain valuable nutrients, cleanse toxins from your body, and strengthen your immune system.

Appendix B

FRUIT AND VEGETABLE SEASONAL AVAILABILITY
(BY HEMISPHERE)

Availability may vary due to the climate of your region. In temperate regions, many growing seasons are extended; check with your local farmers' market or produce market for more information. Smartphone apps for seasonal produce availability are also available in some areas.

Vegetables:	*Northern Hemisphere*	*Southern Hemisphere*
Acorn Squash	September – November	March – June
Artichokes	March – May	August - November
Arugula	May – October	November – April
Asparagus	May and June	August - December
Avocado	March – May	September – November
Beans	August to October	Summer and autumn
Beets	July – December	January – June
Belgian Endive	Late autumn and winter, (most are "forced" to grow under artificial conditions)	Late autumn and winter, (most are "forced" to grow under artificial conditions)
Bell Pepper	June – December	January – May
Bitter Melon	April – September	October – March
Broad Beans	June and July	December and January
Broccoli	Best in autumn, can be year-round in temperate climates.	Best in autumn/ winter, can be year-round in temperate climates.
Broccoli (sprouting)	February and March	August and September
Broccolini	Same as Broccoli	Same as Broccoli
Brussels Sprouts	November – February	May – August
Butternut Squash	October – January	April – July

Vegetables:	Northern Hemisphere	Southern Hemisphere
Cabbage-Chinese	Autumn	May – July
Cabbage-Green & Red	Autumn	Year-round
Cardoons	September to March	Summer/autumn
Carrots	Spring and autumn, year round in temperate climates. The deeper the orange color, the more Beta Carotene. Larger core = sweeter.	Spring and autumn, year round in temperate climates. The deeper the orange color, the more Beta Carotene. Larger core = sweeter.
Cauliflower	Autumn	April – December
Chiles (hot)	End of summer/ early autumn (need heat to ripen)	End of summer/ early autumn (need heat to ripen)
Corn	Autumn (best when tightly closed, fresh looking husks and tassels)	August – November (best when tightly closed, fresh looking husks and tassels)
Cucumbers	Summer (great for cooling down; they are usually 20° cooler than outside temperature)	Summer and autumn (great for cooling down; they are usually 20° cooler than outside temperature)
Curry Leaves	N/A	Year-round
Eggplant	September – December	March – May
Fennel	Summer/autumn	Winter/spring

Vegetables:	Northern Hemisphere	Southern Hemisphere
Garbanzo Beans-fresh (a.k.a. Chick Peas)	Summer – (in warmer climates)	Spring
Garlic	Late summer/early autumn	July – February
Green Beans	Mid-summer – autumn	Mid-summer – autumn
Green Onion	Spring	Autumn
Herbs	Summer – look for vibrant leaves and fresh looking stems.	Can be year-round. Not many in winter.
Leeks	Fall/early winter	Spring and summer
Lemongrass	Summer – think of it as perfume for your food!	Year-round
Lettuce	Spring/summer - best in cooler climates	Summer and autumn
New Potatoes	Spring	Spring
Peas	Spring – summer	Spring
Potatoes	Year-round	Autumn and winter
Pumpkins	Autumn/winter	Summer and autumn
Radishes	Spring	Spring
Rhubarb	Spring	Spring and summer
Silverbeet	Year-round	Winter and spring
Snow Peas	Spring/early summer	Summer and autumn
Spinach	March – May, October – December	April and May, September – November

Vegetables:	Northern Hemisphere	Southern Hemisphere
Spring Onion	Spring	Summer and autumn
Summer Squash	Summer	Summer
Sweet Potato	September – December	March – May
Swiss Chard	Autumn	Autumn
Turnips	Spring	Spring
Tomatoes	July to September	Summer and autumn
Zucchini	June – September	December – March

Fruit:	Northern Hemisphere	Southern Hemisphere
Apples	Autumn – early winter	Autumn
Apricots	May – July	November – January
Asian Pears	July – September	January – March
Bananas	Year-round	Year-round
Berries	Varies, check with your local farmers' market or grocer	Varies, check with your local farmers' market or grocer
Black Currants	June –August	January
Blackberries	July and August	Summer
Blueberries	May – August	November – March
Boysenberries	Autumn	December and January
Cantaloupes	Summer (make sure they feel heavy and smell like melons!)	Summer (make sure they feel heavy and smell like melons!)

Fruit:	Northern Hemisphere	Southern Hemisphere
Cherries(Sweet)	May – August (best eaten right after picking)	December to February (best eaten right after picking)
Cherries (Sour)	August and September	February and March
Figs	Summer (mid-late), 2nd shorter season in November in warm climates	Autumn
Grapefruit	Spring	Winter and spring
Grapes	July to September	Summer and autumn
Kiwis	Spring	Autumn and winter
Kumquats	Early spring	Spring
Lemons	Spring	January to June
Limes	Summer – look for small, heavy fruits.	Late spring to early autumn
Loganberries	Late autumn	December and January
Mangoes	Late spring-summer, (need tropical heat to ripen)	Late spring-summer, (need tropical heat to ripen)
Melons	Summer (should be heavy for their size)	Summer/autumn
Mulberries	May	
Nashi	July – September	February and March
Nectarines	Summer	Summer and autumn
Oranges (Valencia)	Summer	Summer
Oranges (Navel)	Autumn and early winter	Winter and spring

Fruit:	Northern Hemisphere	Southern Hemisphere
Pawpaw	September and October	March and April
Peach	Summer	Summer and autumn
Pears	Autumn	Autumn
Persimmons	Autumn	Autumn
Pineapple	April and May	October and November
Plums	June and July	Summer and autumn
Quince	Autumn	Autumn
Raspberries	Late spring – summer	December - May
Strawberries	Best in spring (can be year round in temperate climates)	Summer (can be year round in temperate climates)
Tayberries & Silvanberries	Summer	December and January

Appendix C

MINERALS/TRACE MINERALS IN REPLETE AQUA™

MINERAL CONTENT IN REPLETE AQUA™ (ppm)		
	Replete Aqua™	Raw
TDS (Total Dissolved Solids)	55077	42509
Source of TDS	NAT	NAT
Hardness	8048	6985.6
pH	7.8	7.4
Bicarbonates	177	154
Calcium	520	454
Copper	0.37	0.01
Iron	1.24	0.01
Magnesium	1700	1474
Manganese	0.24	0.04
Phosphorous	0	0.28
Potassium	960	554
Silica	370	240.5
Sodium	14000	11796
Zinc	1.24	0.01
Actinium	trace	trace
Aluminum	trace	trace
Antimony	trace	trace
Argon	trace	trace
Arsenic	trace	trace
Astatine	trace	trace

Beryllium	trace	trace
Bismuth	trace	trace
Boron	trace	trace
Bromine	trace	trace
Cadmium	trace	trace
Carbon	trace	trace
Cerium	trace	trace
Cesium	trace	trace
Chlorine	trace	trace
Chromium	trace	trace
Cobalt	trace	trace
Copper	trace	trace
Europium	trace	trace
Fluorine	trace	trace
Galdolium	trace	trace
Gallium	trace	trace
Germanium	trace	trace
Gold	trace	trace
Helium	trace	trace
Hydrogen	trace	trace
Indium	trace	trace
Iodine	trace	trace
Iridium	trace	trace
Iron	trace	trace
Krypton	trace	trace
Lanthanum	trace	trace
Lead	trace	trace
Lithium	trace	trace
Mercury	trace	trace
Molybdenum	trace	trace

Neodymium	trace	trace
Neon	trace	trace
Nickel	trace	trace
Niobium	trace	trace
Nitrogen	trace	trace
Osmappeium	trace	trace
Oxygen	trace	trace
Palladium	trace	trace
Phosphorus	trace	trace
Platinum	trace	trace
Plutonium	trace	trace
Polonium	trace	trace
Praseodynium	trace	trace
Proactinum	trace	trace
Radim	trace	trace
Radon	trace	trace
Rhenium	trace	trace
Rhodium	trace	trace
Rubidium	trace	trace
Ruthenium	trace	trace
Scandium	trace	trace
Selenium	trace	trace
Silicone	trace	trace
Silver	trace	trace
Strontium	trace	trace
Sulphur	trace	trace
Sumarium	trace	trace
Technetium	trace	trace
Tellurium	trace	trace
Terbium	trace	trace

Thallium	trace	trace
Thorium	trace	trace
Tin	trace	trace
Titanium	trace	trace
Tungsten	trace	trace
Uranium	trace	trace
Vanadium	trace	trace
Xenon	trace	trace
Yttrium	trace	trace
Zirconium	trace	trace

BIBLIOGRAPHY/RESOURCES

Herman Aihara, *The History of Macrobiotics*

Arthur K. Balin, M.D. Ph.D., Loretta Platt Balin, M.D., *The Life of the Skin*, Bantam, 1997

Glenn Woodruff, Piano Master/Owner J-B Piano Co., San Rafael, CA *http://www.jbpiano.com/*

Rudolf Steiner, *Deeper Insights into Education*, Anthroposophic Press, 1983

Robert Ballard, Director of the Center for Ocean Exploration *http://www.nautiluslive.org.*

John and Jan Belleme, *Japanese Foods That Heal*, Tuttle Publishing, 2007

Pamela Johnson Fenner & Karen Rivers, *Waldorf Education*, Michaelmas Press, 1995

Joseph Kurlan, *Living in Beauty*, EMC Publishing, 2000

Leader of the Future, The Drucker Foundation, Jossey-Bass Publishers, 1996

Margaret Mitchell, President and Founder; Epi Center MedSpa, San Francisco, CA *http://www.skinrejuv.com/*

Michio Kushi, *The Book of Macrobiotics, The Universal way of Health and Happiness*, Japan Publications, Inc., 1977

"Nature's Medicine, Plants That Heal." *National Geographic Society*, 2000

Amy Rost, *Natural Healing Wisdom*, Black Dog & Leventhal Publishing, 2009

Joseph J. Weed, *Wisdom of the Mystic Masters*, Parker Publishing Company, 1968

Hank Fieger, *Behavior Change, a view from the inside out*, Morgan James Publishing, LLC, 2009

Lappe JM, Travers-Gustafson D, Davies KM, Recker RR, Heaney RP. "Vitamin D and Calcium Supplementation Reduces Cancer Risk: Results of a Randomized Trial." *American Journal of Clinical Nutrition*. (2007) 85.6 1586-1591.

National Institute of Health Office of Dietary Supplements: "Dietary Supplement Fact Sheet: Vitamin D." 2004 National Institute of Health Office of Dietary Supplements June 11, 2007.

EWG's Skin Deep staff scientists compare the ingredients on personal care product labels and websites to information in nearly 60 toxicity and regulatory databases at about one million page views per month. *http://www.ewg.org/skindeep/site/about.php*

"Stress: How It Affects Your Body, and How You Can Stay Healthier." By Elizabeth Scott, M.S., About.com Guide Updated May 14, 2011; About.com Health's Disease and Condition content is reviewed by the Medical Review Board

Loretta Pratt Balin, M.D (Quote in Chapter Three)

Ed Esko, Amberwaves Journal 1:1 (2001). http://www.amberwaves.
org/index.html [12/24/2013]

INDEX

Influential Philosophers, Thinkers, Teachers, Doers:

Michio Kushi helped introduce modern macrobiotics to the United States in the early 1950s. He has lectured about philosophy, spiritual development, health, food, and diseases at conferences and seminars all over the world. Kushi studied with macrobiotic educator, George Ohsawa, in Japan.

Rudolf Steiner is a well-known Austrian philosopher, thinker, and social reformer. He spoke and wrote prolifically about the spiritual movement he founded called anthroposophy, which is based on idealist philosophy with links to theosophy. He termed it spiritual science that looked at the inner spiritual needs of humans. He centered his work on the influence of children through Waldorf education, agriculture, and the natural world; he believed there are no essential limits to human knowledge. Steiner was adamant that ethics, meditation, and awareness would help people become moral, creative, and motivated by good intentions. Steiner also co-founded the pharmaceutical company, Weleda, in 1921, which distributes natural medicinal products worldwide. He was also a forerunner in the area of biodynamic farming and sustainability to increase soil fertility without chemical fertilizers and pesticides.

Edgar Cayce (1877-1945) was an American psychic who could channel healing answers to questions while in a trance. Although this requires non-linear thinking, Cayce's remedies are still being used today. He had an uncanny ability to memorize the pages of a book simply by sleeping on it. It is clear he was able to access some parts of his body, cellular structure, or brain that most of us do not use. He had a gift and a desire to help others.

The primary subject of Cayce's readings with subjects like discovering your mission in life, developing your intuition, exploring ancient mysteries, and taking responsibility for your health, showed an alignment with universal law. There are also recommendations for a variety of health concerns, - from acne, diet, cancer, arthritis, mental illness, and psoriasis.

The information from the readings on health include simple suggestions that each of us can do to stay well. The nature of many of these recommendations indicate that Cayce's understanding of physical care was really ahead of its time. These basic principles include these topics: maintaining a well-balanced diet, regular exercise, the role of attitudes and emotions, the importance of relaxation and recreation, and keeping our physical bodies cleansed, both on the outside and the inside.

Robert Ballard is a world-renowned oceanographer. He is best known for the discoveries of deep sea hydrothermal vents (black smokers) the wrecks of the RMS Titanic in 1985, the battleship Bismarck in 1989, and the aircraft carrier USS Yorktown in 1998. He is president of the **Institute for Exploration** and Director of the **Center for Ocean Exploration** at the University of Rhode Island's Graduate School of Oceanography. Explore the ocean live with Dr. Ballard and his Corps of Explorers aboard the E/V Nautilus at http://www.nautiluslive.org.

George Ohsawa was born into a poor samurai family during the Meiji Restoration. He had no money for higher education, but he is the founder of macrobiotics.

Thousands of years ago, great sages realized that the food we eat not only sustains life, but also underlies our health and happiness. A few examples of the religious or medical laws they compiled are as follows: the Code of Manu in India, the Hebrew code, the Nei Ching and the Hon.so Komoku (the first medicinal herb book) in China, the Zen diet in Japan.

Going against this trend, Ishizuka criticized the adoption of the West's modern medicine and dietary theories, and recommended the Japanese traditional diet of whole, unrefined foods with very little or no milk or animal foods.

He cured many patients by having them eat a traditional diet based on brown rice and a variety of land and sea vegetables. Since his method was unique at that time and effective, many patients visited his clinic, so many, in fact, that he had to limit his practice to a hundred persons per day. There were also many inquiries by mail, which because of his fame would reach him addressed only "Vegetable Doctor, Tokyo," "Daikon (Japanese radish) Doctor, Tokyo," or "Anti-Doctor Doctor, Tokyo." His healing technique was based on the recognition of five very important principles: foods are the foundation of health and happiness; sodium and potassium are the primary antagonistic and complementary elements in food. They most strongly determine its character or "yin/yang" quality. Grain is properly the staple food of man. Food should be unrefined, whole, and natural. Food should be grown locally and eaten in season.

In Greek, "macro" means big or great and "biotic" means concerning life, so the word "macrobiotic" refers to the "big view of life." This meaning suggests that we should relax our small, rigid views of the world so that the underlying unity of nature can be sensed. The word "macrobiotic" was originally used in literature by the German scholar Christophe Wilhelm Von Hufeland in Das Makrobiotik (1796).

Macrobiotics is based on an understanding of the rhythm, the ebb and flow of nature. Its roots can be traced back through civilization to the beginning of human tradition. Although it requires study and seemingly very big adjustments, macrobiotics is a practical way of living towards happiness. Michio Kushi was the first such student who left Japan from his school.

ACKNOWLEDGEMENTS

I am grateful to my parents for giving me a strong foundation through seasonal living and plenty of love. They showed me how to welcome change by finding all the good it brings with it. I am grateful for my two sisters who have always been close to my heart, despite any geographic distance. I'd like to thank them for keeping our traditions alive by passing them on to our children.

SPECIAL THANKS

Cover design: Alejandra Chavira

Clothes designer: Karen Caldwell, Robin Brouilette

Cover shot: Shankha Goswami

Contributor & travel expert: Ashley Horowitz

Corporate Attorney for Intellectual Property/COO: Josh Horowitz

Editors: Mary Ann Shelton, Mariko England

Furs: Fur Salon at Saks

Jewelry: Graff Diamonds, Judith Ripka

Photography: Liza Gershman, Deva Sexton, Shankha Goswami, Drew Altizer, Cindy Shelton, Elaine Foo

Photoshoot Choreography: Charleston Pierce

Piano Master, Composer, and Poet: Glenn Woodruff

Publishing Assistance: SAbER Mountain Publishers

Resource for Medical and Cosmetic Enhancement Therapy: Margaret Mitchell

ELISABETH THIERIOT

My Be Fabulous At Any Age Notes:

Get a set of free samples of five of our products!

You just have to go to our website
www.repleteskincare.com
and enter the code
globalskin

SOON, YOU WILL HAVE HER SKIN TOO.

Get a set of free samples of five of our products!

You just have to go to our website
www.repleteskincare.com
and enter the code
globalskin

SOON, YOU WILL HAVE HER SKIN TOO.